WE EAT OUR ROADKILL
TALES FROM HORTON BAY, MICHIGAN

We Eat Our Roadkill
Tales from Horton Bay, Michigan

Ted Walker

NEC SORTE NEC FACTO

Rutherford Press
05134 Horton Bay Road
Boyne City, Michigan 49712

First Printing, September, 1997

Illustrations and Cartoons:

The Horton Bay Morals Committee has not yet rated this book, though it is generally considered to be suitable for readers of all ages.
Printed in the United States of America

ISBN 0-9660582-0-8

For

Tracey with all my love,
and the
Road Warriors, Pelican Chapter

Dave Berry, Grand Pooba
Paula Berry, Bailiff and Bouncer
Bob Mettler, Parliamentarian (Roberts Rules of Order)
Vivian Mettler, Social Director and Club Photographer
Joe Beaudoin, Treasurer
Sandy Beaudoin, Club Historian (Gossip)
Tracey Walker, Gastrointestinal Sound Effects
Oliver Jones, Token Minority

1

Introduction
WE EAT OUR ROAD KILL
Tales from Horton Bay, Michigan

My family first vacationed in Northern Michigan when I was just a young child. We took the train from Union Station in St. Louis, Missouri to Chicago where we changed trains and headed for the tiny town of Charlevoix in Michigan's northern lower peninsula. Today I can jump on the interstate and make the drive in about eleven hours. The train trip, when I was a wide eyed child, took two full days.

It was a long and arduous trip, but the journey was well worth the effort. St. Louis summers are terribly hot and humid, and in the early 1950's air conditioning was relatively new, very expensive and practically nonexistent.

It got so hot in St. Louis that a freshly laundered shirt immediately turned limp and wet with perspiration while dressing in the morning. A person's hair remained damp from the humidity, and dangled in stringy rows or curly frizz depending on its texture. Nobody was in a hurry to get anywhere. People fanned themselves with whatever happened to be available, a newspaper, an advertising flyer, an open hand. It was impossible to stay in the broiling sun for any length of time without feeling slightly light headed and weak. Every year the radio stations broadcast heat alerts and the young, the elderly and the infirm were warned to stay in the shade and to keep wet rags on their heads in a feeble attempt to keep cool. But nothing seemed to work. Every summer the Post Dispatch and Globe Democrat newspapers reported the deaths of people who had succumbed to the blistering heat. It was as though a St. Louis summer was

3

nature's way of culling out the weak.

Even rambunctious children fell victims to the incessant summer heat. When first let out to play boys and girls alike made their bold dash for freedom, the adult's warnings to slow down and be careful of the heat trailing after them. The children whooped as they streaked across the dry, brown grass, stirring up tiny tornadoes of powdery dust. It never took long for the children to collapse in the shade, their faces red and glistening with sweat. Dark lines of dirt gathered in the creases of their necks and they panted like dogs as they desperately tried to cool down. Sometimes a garden hose was pulled out and everyone took turns squirting the others. The girls usually made a big show of protesting the drenching, but in reality they shoved and pushed with the boys for the opportunity to stand in the line of fire. Many evenings in late summer I remember running through the lawn sprinkler my father used in our yard in his feckless attempt to keep the grass from dying. We'd jump over the sprinkler and dash through the rotating circle of cool water drops that momentarily formed a luxurious canopy over our heads. The dusk would be lit by hundreds of fireflies. Eventually, my mother would call to us to be quiet. Our screams of delight had carried down the block, even in the wet, muggy air. Mr. Johnson, who lived down the street and who we called the "Mean Man" because he didn't allow us to cut through his yard on our way to and from the school bus, had complained one evening that our shouting was bursting through his open windows, and ruining his radio program. So in the twilight, just after the fireflies appeared, about the time the crickets started humming, I knew mother would be calling me in for the night.

My mother firmly believed that the hot summers brought out the mischief in children. Years later at my older sister's wedding reception my mother fondly told the story of the summer my sister called a pizza restaurant and ordered two pizzas to be delivered to the home of a girl she had quarreled with earlier that day. The next night fifteen pizzas from six different pizza parlors were delivered to our house. The battle of the pizzas had begun. The pizza restaurants never could prove anything, but my sister and the other girl were both grounded for one week. Then I got grounded for standing outside Mrs. Tewer's house and chanting, "Old lady Tewer fell in a sewer and came out smelling like manure." I knew, and so did my parents, that the sticky summer heat was the real culprit.

The temperature always became a topic in any conversation.

"Another hot one," one person would say as a greeting to another.

"It sure is," would be the reply. "My wife's pregnant and I don't mind telling you that I'm worried about her being in this heat."

4

"If any of us had a lick of sense we'd move to a cooler part of the country."

"I just wish I had the money for a vacation. A nice vacation. I'd head for the north woods."

Air conditioning was a new invention. Anyone who bought one of the huge, boxy window units for their house was considered to have more money than sense. After all, who knew if the noisy contraptions really worked. A few businesses installed air conditioning with the hope that it would improve sales. Movie theatres were among the most savvy. Their management correctly reasoned that people would use the theatres as a refuge from the stifling summer heat. They were right. People gladly paid their money for a ticket and contented themselves with spending hours in the dark, cool theatres, watching the same feature two, three or sometimes even four times in a row. But eventually everyone had to go home to rooms that when baked by the day's heat more closely resembled a hothouse. Good sleep was impossible. My mother used to put the top sheets in the bathtub and soak them in cold water. Then the beds would be remade. I was too young to remember with any clarity those nights of brutal heat, but I do recall how in later years my mother described those long, hot nights of tossing and turning, wrestling a soggy sheet that only stayed cool for an hour or so. Those were the nights when a person languished in the muggy dark, nostalgically thinking of a sparkling autumn day with the same relish a man dying of thirst dreams of a cool drink of bubbling spring water.

Our family was fortunate. My father was a successful insurance executive and could afford to take us on summer vacations. The quaint town of Charlevoix, Michigan had become popular with a number of St. Louis people. The town is nestled on a strip of sandy land between Lake Michigan and Round Lake, a small lake that opens onto beautiful Lake Charlevoix. The town was, and remains to this day, an ideal place to vacation.

My father rented a cottage in the Belvedere Association, a summer colony of neat, brightly painted cottages that overlooked Round Lake and Lake Charlevoix. Belvedere was comprised of genteel, refined people who were content to enjoy the privilege of extended trips, relaxing with their cocktails on wide cottage porches and who seemingly hadn't a care in the world. The languid conversation tended to focus on matters such as how much to spend on a daughter's dress for the next season's winter cotillion when a new batch of future Women's Leaguers would be introduced to society.

In recent years, as the respectable "old money" generation died off, a slightly more hubris resident has moved into Belvedere. These people, I believe, are quite taken with themselves as they scoot briskly in their electric golf carts from one cottage to another, their cocktails sloshing about. They talk endlessly of money, the stock market and their golf game. The staid women dress stylishly, albeit very conservatively. Standard men's wear might be cream colored slacks embroidered with miniature golf clubs, sailboats or tiny spouting whales, navy blue blazers and starched golf shirts that cost more than a nice dinner for two. These people wouldn't dare be caught in a Wal-Mart where a golf shirt on sale is cheaper than a dozen golf balls. They constantly have a smirk on their faces as if they are the keeper of some special secret and they gawk at people who drive by the Association's gates as though they are outsiders, and, in fact, the passersby are outsiders, who live in a distant world. Some of the outsiders slow their cars to gawk back, desperately longing to be inside those gates, the so called promised land, living beneath an invisible bubble of isolation.

But there are always exceptions to the rule and I now know several Belvedere people who are good people. They have cottages there simply because they like the location or the pretty view or the wind off the lake. They are there for the experience of a summer in Northern Michigan, not for some perceived status of Belvedere.

But even Belvedere is a part of the fabric that makes up Northern Michigan, and today if I stand away from the cluster of cottages I can still see the innocent scenes from my youth. I remember bright, clear mornings, balmy afternoons with the temperature in the low eighties. It's quite easy, especially on the water, to get a terrific sunburn. I could always spot the new arrivals because they either had no color or were red as cooked lobsters. Anyone who had been in Northern Michigan for a couple of weeks had dark tans. At night I wore flannel pajamas and slept beneath blankets. The foot of my narrow bed always cradled a big, down comforter. There is nothing better than swimming and sunning during the day and wearing sweaters and sleeping beneath blankets at night.

Even rainy days held a certain cachet. Those days usually began with a heavy mist, which is a combination of light rain mixed with sprays lifted off the lakes by a strong breeze. The mist held a crisp smell, clean and a bit electrical, and whenever the wind shifted and blew over the land the air smelled of wet pine needles, cedar and freshly mowed grass. The sky would darken as heavy clouds pushed in from Lake Michigan. There might be flashes of lightning and loud, booming thunder. And then came the rain. It fell slowly at first, big, fat drops that made a smacking sound on the uninsulated cottage roofs. As the storm gathered strength, the wind blew through the high branches of the trees and the rain began to fall so that the world outside my window became a grey blur of water. We'd turn on the table lamps and sit in the open windows watching the storm march across the sky. The rain spattered against the window screens, and our faces became wet, and I remember to this day how very special and happy a rainy day in Michigan made me feel.

The two day trip from Missouri had all the trappings of a journey of great import. There was luggage, mountains of it. My mother packed two steamer trunks that required two robust porters to hoist into the baggage car. There were suitcases, too. Big ones, small ones, overnight bags. My mother carried a frilly parasol in one hand, her feeble attempt at keeping the baking St. Louis sun off her face, and a miniature suitcase in the other. This was her makeup and jewelry case. It contained some of the most cherished necessities in her life; lipstick the color of rose petals, powders, blush, nail polish, the string of real pearls that my father had given her on their tenth wedding anniversary. Before I'd ever even seen Northern Michigan I sensed I was headed for someplace special when my mother first packed this bag and refused to let it out of her sight.

I remember when the train pulled into the Charlevoix station. Lake Charlevoix was to our left, the east. The water was as true a blue as I've ever seen. Close to the white sandy beach (sugar sand beaches, as the real estate people call them in their ads) the water turned a pale blue, the color of new ice when it is very cold. We didn't disembark at the Charlevoix station. The Belvedere people had their own station, which was only a few hundred yards down the line, but it was a symbol, a statement, that Belvedere people were special. To get off at the Charlevoix depot would mean the inconvenience of a ten minute ride around Round Lake and going through town. And so we watched, us kids anxiously and in awe, the grownups impatiently, as the other people, the outsiders, waited on the platform for their luggage. Finally, the train sluggishly lunged forward, and belching smoke and steam, crossed the trembling wood bridge (the bridge remained for years after the railroad ceased to function, and finally, when considered an eye sore, was torn down) that spanned the narrow strait that separates Round Lake and Lake Charlevoix. With a jolting, lurching stop we had arrived at the Belvedere station, or the casino as it is called in reference to earlier days when there had been some illegal gambling in the building.

What a joy it was each year to officially be back in Northern Michigan. The sky was the same color as the water, a cool breeze, often

7

carrying the faint, sweet fragrance of cherry trees, pushed across the land from Lake Michigan. We always seemed to arrive back in Northern Michigan on one of those perfect summer days when it takes all the will power a person can muster not to throw open their arms and thank God for being alive. St. Louis was far, far away, a lingering bad memory, a black cloud I could forget about, at least for another six weeks.

Even though we were surrounded by water most parents normally turned us children out to play on our own. We were given the stern warning to never go near the water unless it was during a supervised swim. Naturally, we ignored these warnings. How could any kid not be tempted to explore, and fully experience the wonder of these magnificent lakes. We fished, we skipped stones, we skinny dipped. We found small objects, a discarded buoy, a piece of driftwood, and pushed them out into the water where we bombarded them with thrown stones. Once we used Chipper Ransom's brand new toy cabin cruiser. It took us maybe five minutes to send her to the bottom of Round Lake. We sat on the beach and watched as sailboats, heeled over by a strong wind, tacked back and forth. Wednesday afternoons we watched the races and marveled with a child's fascination as the boats flew their huge multicolored spinnakers, jibing towards Boyne City. Occasionally we "borrowed" an untended row boat, and with oars flailing away, paddled out into the lake where the water became so blue it was almost black. One time a yellow lab followed us out in the lake. The dog became so tired we had to pull him into the boat. We capsized and had to cling to the hull until the coast guard arrived. Everyone survived, including the dog, but, we all caught hell from our parents. Nothing changed. The next day we were doing the same thing. And it's not that our parent's were lax. It's just that in those days there was no feeling of insecurity or trouble. It was extremely rare that any sort of tragedy touched Northern Michigan. There was barely any crime. No one bothered to lock their cottage doors. Children were safe to walk the quiet, shaded streets.

We only spent three summers in Belvedere. I am proud of my father for many reasons and even more so whenever I think back to our third summer when there was a major problem and we left, my father vowing that we would never return. There are a great many rules, written and unwritten, in Belvedere by which residents are supposed to live their lives. A written rule might be that you had to be approved by a committee just to be able to rent a cottage. You had to rent for at least three years before you could buy a cottage, and then you had to be approved again. You only owned the cottage, not the land beneath it, and Association personnel took care of that land. They tended to the maintenance, the taking down of a dead tree, the pruning of a wayward bush. To hire a private contractor for these jobs was against the rules.

The two most important unwritten rules were that the only black people allowed on the grounds were to be uniformed domestic help. And Jews! My God, a Jew had never before set foot in Belvedere; that is, until my father invited his good friend and insurance client from St. Louis, Harry Tennenbaum and his wife, for cocktails on the front porch. Undoubtedly, my father casually mentioned this affair to someone, and before very long the President of the Belvedere Association was knocking on our front door. He confronted my father with the rumor that had been circulating from cottage to cottage like an uncontrollable California brush fire. Yes, my father calmly informed the President, he had indeed invited a lovely couple, the Tennenbaums, for cocktails. As my mother told the story years later, the President, his face red and eyes bulging, angrily shook his finger under my father's nose and promised him that if he entertained these people on Belvedere property he himself would never again be welcome there. "Understand?" the President screamed. "Yes," my father calmly replied. "I fully understand."

That evening my parents and the Tennenbaums enjoyed a wonderful evening on the front porch, casually enjoying each other's company and ignoring the neighbor's stares. We stayed another week, just long enough for my father to prove that he hadn't been run out of Belvedere. I love my father so very much. There is nothing worse than bigotry. Nothing.

At the time I only knew that we were leaving what I now considered paradise. For me, there would never again be bare assed swims in the lake or games of tag on the beach. Evening fun on the Belvedere green, the lawn adjacent to where the old Belvedere Hotel once stood, would be forever lost. I'd never play Kick the Can or Red Rover, Red Rover again.

The next summer I was sent away to camp and, I admit, I enjoyed myself. Yet for years the memory of Northern Michigan marinated and simmered in my mind until returning became an obsession.

Much later as a grown man toiling away in the advertising business in St. Louis I very frequently day dreamed about those long ago summers and pampered myself with the hope that one day I could move to Charlevoix. I reasoned that if I could just be back in Michigan everything in my life would be miraculously transformed. All my problems would evaporate. Every tawdry aspect would conveniently disappear. I would never again experience loss, abandonment or betrayal. There would be no more emptiness. No more sorrow. Never again would I taste bitter defeats. My failing marriage would suddenly be fine, my children would forever smile at me. I would be a good father, a faithful husband. I wouldn't have reasons to drink so much. There would be no more nerve numbing commutes in rush hour traffic. No more vicious corporate politics. No more hazy, steamy summer days with nothing to do.

I'd always wanted to write, not advertising copy, but serious prose. Short stories, novels. My innermost ambition had always been to move to Northern Michigan and devote my time to writing. I had no idea if I had what it took to be a successful writer. Maybe I didn't, but I figured that if I could live in Northern Michigan I'd be free of my demons and fears. I'd be back in paradise and ready to give writing a try. It was all I could think about.

When I was in my late thirties I decided to start a small broadcast company. I used money from my profit sharing and pension fund to buy two radio stations in Southeast Missouri. Then I got divorced. In 1991 I married Tracey Silkwood, a wonderful woman I'd met when she went to work at one of my stations. So much for not dipping one's pen in company ink! We spent our honeymoon in Northern Michigan. Over the next two years we visited Charlevoix three more times. By now Tracey also had fallen in love with the area. More and more I began to dwell on the possibility of selling my business, moving to Charlevoix and giving writing a serious try. Long before we got married Tracey had left the radio station to pursue a nursing degree in order to become a Registered Nurse. Both Charlevoix and Petoskey have wonderful hospitals so now the prospect of a move began to take form. We visited Charlevoix again and on this trip bought some land with the idea that if we did move we'd build a house.

If there had been any lingering doubts about moving to Michigan they were quickly erased by one of life's coincidences that confirm that fate actually exists. Upon returning to Missouri I found a message from a cable TV company in Nashville stating that it was interested in expanding into radio. Would I be interested in selling my stations? My enthusiasm no doubt cost me money when we started negotiating a sale price, but I couldn't care less. I was more interested in moving to Charlevoix.

Things started to roll pretty fast once I agreed to sell my business. We put our house on the market and quickly accepted an offer. Tracey was offered a position as an Intensive Care Registered Nurse at Northern Michigan Hospital in Petoskey. She was told that they needed her immediately. We packed all our belongings in a trailer and the largest

10

rental truck we could get, threw the dog in Tracey's car and drove all day, arriving in Charlevoix late at night in a snow storm. We rented a room, unloading the house plants and carrying them across the empty parking lot to our room where they would be spared a severe frostbite.

The next morning brought a cold, clear day. We had coffee and stared out across Lake Charlevoix, still frozen over and magnificently serene. The sun glinted off the whiteness with such intensity that it burned our eyes, and so we sat in our tiny room wearing sunglasses and enjoying the quiet peace of a winter day.

Tracey reported to her new job while I set about the task of finding a house to rent. Everything had happened so fast that we didn't have a minute to think about building a house on our lot. Even if we had a set of blueprints it would be months before there would be a finished house for us to move into. I drove downtown to Vacation Property Network, the largest real estate company in town, and inquired about a house to rent. I quickly learned that there is a real shortage of rental property. The only house we found after several hours of looking was a dump that rented for $750 per month, utilities extra and no pets. The owner flatly stated that the price and conditions were firm. Our real estate agent correctly suggested that for $400 to $700 a month we'd be better off buying a small house to live in while we built our house in Charlevoix. We looked at several houses in our price range and nothing thrilled us. Finally, our agent asked if we'd consider looking in Horton Bay, which is about ten miles from Charlevoix.

I'd heard a great deal about Horton Bay, and driven through the tiny village several times. The village is approximately halfway between Charlevoix and Boyne City on the shores of Lake Charlevoix and the sheltered, expansive bay that gave the village its name. The village is famous for quite a few reasons. The Nobel prize winning writer, Ernest Hemingway, spent the summers of his youth at the family cottage on nearby Walloon Lake. Young Hemingway escaped the pressures of dealing with his overbearing mother and work at Longfield Farm, the family farm, by visiting Horton Bay where he was free to spend his days loafing and fishing for trout in Horton Creek or any variety of fish in the bay. He frequently spent the night in Horton Bay often staying in the rear of Pinehurst, the Dilworth family restaurant. Much later in his life Hemingway remembered Horton Bay in several of his short stories. The short story, UP IN MICHIGAN, describes the old General Store, which is now on the National Historic Registry and another reason Horton Bay has become famous.

Horton Bay is also justifiably famous because at one time the miniscule town boasted three of Northern Michigan's best restaurants. Auntie Beth Dilworth operated Pinehurst and served what some people still remember as the best fried chicken ever eaten. Her daughter-in-law, Kathryn, who married Wesley Dilworth, ran the Horton Bay House just across the road. Next door to the General store Lizzie and Vollie Fox opened the Red Fox Inn, another restaurant that brought visitors from far away for a delicious chicken dinner. Many people credit Vollie Fox with teaching the young Hemingway how to fly fish and it was Vollie Fox who once bragged to the Boyne City Chamber of Commerce that, "the fish we almost caught in Horton Creek are bigger than the ones you almost caught in the Boyne River."

To this day the Dilworth and Fox families are still living in Horton Bay. And to this day the families still enjoy a good natured debate of the question of who first invented Horton Bay Tomato Pudding. In Horton Bay it's known as the Great Pudding War. The Dilworths and the Foxes each take credit for creating this culinary delight, and each family has a different recipe that they will quickly inform anyone who asks is the official pudding recipe, not to mention the best tasting. What stands as fact, however, is that the three restaurants saved Horton Bay from blowing away with the autumn leaves once the bustling timber business failed in Northern Michigan.

The village later earned a reputation for being a wild, more than slightly zany community thanks to the imaginations of several long time residents. In the late 1970's Bill Ohle, whose family nearly a century ago operated the Stroud and Ohle sawmill in Horton Bay, decided the village needed to have a Fourth of July parade. Bill's idea was that the parade had to be different. It had to be creative and loaded with madcap fun in order to attract spectators who were accustomed to attending big city parades or parades in their home town. Today Horton Bay is only comprised of 19 year round residents, hardly enough to make up a parade, much less line a parade route. Bill's rules were extremely simple, but as it turns out, highly effective and popular. There would be no commercial entries, no politicians or political statements and nothing off color or in bad taste. The idea worked. People got creative and put together what only could be described as wacky, fun filled entries. Today the Horton Bay Parade is nationally renowned attracting between 12,000 and 15,000 spectators. There are usually 75 to 100 entries worked by some 500 participants. People come from all over to cheer for a huge dinosaur that spouts water from its mouth, a synchronized lawn mower marching band, the King and Queen of Horton Bay with the Queen regally sitting on her throne, a used

12

toilet bowl. In her white gloved hand she waves her scepter, a toilet bowl plunger, at the spectators. She carries a sign that pleads with the crowd to help out the royal family by throwing money. At the end of the parade route there is nearly $200 in pennies, dimes and nickels on the float. Only in Horton Bay!

Two other phenomenons occurred in Horton Bay that only added to the village mystique. For over 100 years people have reported spotting a huge sea serpent swimming in the bay. Over the years the gentle residents of Horton Bay have discovered that the sea serpent is not dangerous. The serpent was affectionately named Hortense, the Hortness Monster (Hortie for short) and is now on the town's Endangered Species List. Another beast seen in the area for many years has been a Big Foot creature. This animal was named Windigo. Every year Horton Bay sponsors a Windigo hunt. A group of intrepid volunteers is organized to tramp through the woods looking for Windigo. Large deluxe pizzas are used to bait specially designed and patented Windigo snares. The beast has always managed to outsmart the hunters, eating the pizzas while avoiding being caught.

Horton Bay also hosts a Winter Olympics. Jon Hartwell, a native Hortonian and decedent of the Fox family that ran the famous Red Fox Inn, currently heads up the parade and the Winter Olympics, which is a late winter fund raiser for the parade. As Jon reports, "We have to do something here to avoid cabin fever." And that it does! The Horton Bay Winter Olympics has itself become famous. Plows are used to clear a large area on the frozen bay. Areas for the different events are spray painted on the gleaming ice. At the appointed hour hundreds of participants arrive from miles around and pay good money to see how far they can hurl a frozen fish. There's also turkey-curling, ice bowling, ice golf, swimming in a giant hole in the ice. There's a palm reader, who has the ability to read a palm through a ski glove. The Winter Olympics is always a huge success and yet another reason why in Horton Bay fun is always a way of life!

Yes, indeed, I told the real estate agent, I was very familiar with Horton Bay, but living in this crazy community was an entirely different matter. To this day my ex-wife insists that I have a screw loose and that my elevator doesn't go to the top floor, but since I'd never visited a psychiatrist I wasn't sure that I was qualified to live in Horton Bay.

We drove out to look at the house. It is located about three hundred yards from the General Store. The store is considered downtown Horton Bay, the bustling business district. At three hundred yards away the house would be in the suburbs. Tracey and I immediately loved the house, which we interpreted as another sign of fate pushing us along some preordained course.

The seller either was awfully eager to get out of Horton Bay or else figured that we were nuts and very much belonged there. They accepted our first offer with no counter. Within a month we closed on the sale and moved into the house. Initially, our social activity was confined to Charlevoix. Two or three times a week we made the short drive into town and met friends in one of the many bars for drinks. We also started to make a number of new acquaintances. People constantly questioned me about what I planned to do with my time now that I had sold my business and moved to Northern Michigan. I enthusiastically explained that I intended to write; but since our society is fundamentally based on accomplishment I was inevitably asked what I had written so far and who had published it. I patiently replied that I was in the midst of changing careers, that I was just starting out as a writer and therefore had not yet been published. This answer was usually met with a bewildered look as though what I actually was saying was that I'm a lazy bum, who intended to hang out in the bars, which, to tell the truth, really didn't sound that bad to me. But, I was committed to writing so I continued to repeat my story.

It didn't take very long for me to get tired of saying that I was an unpublished writer. The more I told people that I was unpublished the more the word "unpublished" had the ring of failure in my ears. Eventually, I just quit telling people that I was trying to write. I then had the problem of what to say when asked what I was doing for a living.

Upon moving to Michigan I became acutely aware that the state has a ten cent deposit on beer and pop cans. The idea was that if a can is worth ten cents then it wouldn't end up in the lake or in a street gutter. But there are still people who disregard both the deposit and the environment. Usually when I made the drive into Charlevoix I spotted at least five cans along the road side. It became my habit to pull over and pick up the cans. Hell, I figured, fifty cents helped pay for the drive into town. Every Saturday morning I dutifully took a bag of cans to the store where I was paid my two or three dollars. Chump change for some, but I liked the money. That's about the time I began telling people that I was in the scrap aluminium business. Now I had some respect. Those bewildered looks turned to admiration. Once when I told one of the Belvedere men that I was a scrap aluminium dealer he narrowed his eyes, nodded slowly and gave me one of those long, knowing looks, as though he had just encountered another member of some ultra secret fraternity. Of course, I sometimes tempered my profession to suit the crowd. At Whitney's Oyster

14

Bar, a place frequented by kids in their twenties, I made up the story that I was an exotic dancer at the Bombay Club, a fictitious after hours bar over in Gaylord. I even went so far as to tell one young woman that for ten dollars I'd perform a table dance just for her. When her eyes grew big and she seemed truly impressed I narrowed my eyes, nodded my head slowly and gave her that same all knowing look the Belvedere man had given me. Either way, I finally had settled the nagging problem of what to tell people when I was asked what I did for a living. I was beginning to feel comfortable in Northern Michigan and in Horton Bay.

During one of my morning visits to the General Store for a cup of coffee I met Jon Hartwell, the man in charge of the Fourth of July Parade and the Winter Olympics. We quickly became friends and many evenings he stopped by to have a drink on my deck. He'd already heard me say something about wanting to write so I couldn't pull the scrap aluminium bit, and I felt sure he had no interest in a table dance so when he asked me what business I was in I quickly made up the story that I intended to start a newspaper in Horton Bay. And why not? After all, the village had a famous parade, the Winter Olympics, Hortie, the sea monster, Windigo, and the General Store, which is on the National Historic Registry. Ernest Hemingway had also lived in and written about the village. Horton Bay deserved a newspaper, I preached, hoping that my new friend would buy my story. He asked what I would call the paper, and off the top of my head I blurted out, "The Horton Bay Gazette!"

My first summer in Horton Bay Jon and I spent a good deal of time sitting on my deck, comfortably sipping cocktails and talking about The Horton Bay Gazette. My children were visiting for the summer and they sat enthralled as I described my make believe newspaper to Jon. The more I tried to impress my audience the wilder and more extravagant my story became. I began to create a cast of characters who lived in Horton Bay. I put these characters in all sorts of absurd situations. I used the foundation of wackiness that already permeated the village and built an entire city fit to rival Camelot or Brigadoon. Of course, I was only rambling on and the more vodka I drank the more I rambled.

One night Jon surprised me by asking if he could be a part of my new newspaper. My vision of Horton Bay had excited him. Hoping to carry my preposterous tale a bit further I calmly replied that he could be in charge of advertising. I told him that in that position he would also have to research printing and distribution. I figured that this assignment would distract him enough so that we could get on with the real business at hand, enjoying a Northern Michigan summer. I must confess, however, that the more I created characters and strange events the more I secretly wished that Horton Bay actually had its very own newspaper. Then I would have an outlet for my stories.

One night several weeks later Hartwell arrived at my house for our customary evening of cocktails on the deck carrying a sheaf of papers, and bearing a wide grin. He presented me with all the printing costs and details needed to actually print The Horton Bay Gazette. He even had a listing of the local advertising rates. Since our paper would be new and unproven we agreed to offer it for free and undercut the local rates by a wide margin. This, we hoped, would entice advertisers to support our efforts. We also decided to publish three summer issues and contribute any profits to benefit the parade. We lined up a distributor, who would place the paper in Petoskey, Charlevoix, Boyne Falls, Boyne City, East Jordan, Walloon and, of course, Horton Bay.

Still wanting to test the water I instructed Hartwell to, "get out and sell some advertising." I figured if it was a hard sell then we'd just abandon this absurd idea. Once again Jon showed up on my deck, this time he was carrying a bunch of orders! Suddenly we had the foundation for a newspaper. Writing and putting the paper together was my responsibility. The next day I sat down at my computer and began the long and arduous task of putting all my wild stories into print. I must confess that as I wrote the stories I began to doubt that anyone else would find them amusing. Surely, it was only Hartwell and I, lubricated by large sums of vodka, who thought these make believe stories about Horton Bay were funny. But, I continued to write and Hartwell continued to sell advertising. Our first issue was set for June, 1994. It consisted of 28 pages of the off the wall stories I had written and 79 ads! We printed 12,000 copies for distribution, and we were nervous that was probably far too many. Jon and I were flabbergasted when the distributor called a day later and said he had run out of newspapers, which were being picked up as fast as he could distribute them. We immediately decided to print 15,000 copies of the July edition.

The Horton Bay Gazette had immediately become a raging success. Letters and phone calls of praise and congratulations began pouring into the paper. We printed our three issues of The Horton Bay Gazette. Months later by popular demand I printed an edition under the banner The Horton Bay Chronicle, this being done to protect the souvenir hunters who had been promised that only three editions of The Horton Bay Gazette would ever be published.

Over the past two years I've constantly been beseeched by people on the street and former advertisers urging me to reintroduce the

16

newspaper, but I've resisted for many reasons. My foremost one being that there was something very special about the newspaper and I'm afraid that trying to continue might very much be like wearing out a good joke or the sadness related to watching a superb athlete playing well past their prime. There's also a quality of mystique that hovers about our tiny village. Better to let the mystique linger than to turn it into a hard core commercial venture.

But I've had a hard time turning loose of all the fun I'd created. Then I had the idea of putting most of the newspaper stories, along with many new ones, into a single narrative and putting it into book form. A book has more permanence than newspaper issues. Just possibly this effort could be the vehicle that will keep the Horton Bay "Where fun is always a way of life" attitude around for a very long time. I hope that this book brings an occasional smile to your face and that for awhile you'll be transported into our make believe world, forgetting whatever problems that might be nagging you at the time.

I also decided to include two short stories in this book that I wrote after moving to Horton Bay. This small collection reveals my ambition to write some serious prose. Each story exposes a thought or mood that passed fleetingly through my head while sitting alone on my deck or, perhaps, standing on the shoreline of Horton Bay watching the late evening sky turn pink. Sometimes the beauty and tranquility of Horton Bay has literally moved me to tears, and those were the times when I sat down and wrote these stories.

The village of Horton Bay exists though all of the stories contained in this book are fictitious. Except for the mention of Ernest Hemingway, Mary Harris and Brendon LaBlance all the characters are fictitious and any resemblance to persons living or dead is purely coincidental. In mentioning Ernest Hemingway's name I have fictionalized an account of his presence in Horton Bay. I have used Mary Harris' name as an honor to this long time resident of the bay. Mary is now in her late eighties and as full of vitality as ever. She embodies the fun loving spirit of Horton Bay, and it's not hard for the many who know her to imagine her as the furtive, elusive flamingo thief, who is the character I've named after her. Brendon LaBlance is a Charlevoix native whose family has lived in the area for five generations. Brendon has, and always will be, the official, unofficial Horton Bay Fire Chief. Brendon is another person who believes that laughter is the best medicine in life. His input for many of these stories has been invaluable.

And has living in Northern Michigan fulfilled all my dreams? Not quite. I have discovered the simple and obdurate truth that problems follow a person no matter where he or she might live. I still think daily of my parents, now both dead for many years. I remember my best childhood friend who died last year of cancer, and I fondly recall my beautiful cousin, Barbara, who also fell victim to this insidious disease. My heart aches for my beloved Shetland Sheepdog, who disappeared six months ago. And occasionally, I will amble into one of my favorite bars during the summer season where a pretty, young woman will catch my eye and I'll find myself watching her and wishing that I was young again and that we could sit and talk, and that all I had to look forward to was opportunity.

I am happy though, and Northern Michigan is as wonderful a place as any spot in the country. The people are nice, the scenery spectacular and Tracey and I enjoy our life together. Tracey enjoys singing gospel songs, quietly and to herself, as she does her craft work in our living room. There is an open vent between the living room and our bedroom, which is designed to let the hot air rising from the wood stove heat the upstairs. Sometimes at night when I've gone to bed early and Tracey is still downstairs I can hear my gentle wife singing her favorite songs. Her voice is sweet and tender as she sings in praise of the Lord. I lie silently in the dark, listening, and I am filled with a contentment and love for my wife that is so strong I shudder with happiness.

And then there is Horton Bay. It has been said that Ireland is comprised of forty shades of green. If that is true then Horton Bay must have forty one shades. Sometimes I walk down to the bay and sit on the dock, dangling my feet in the water. If it is very quiet and I squint my eyes I can look out across the shimmering water believing that I see Hortie frolicking in the waves. If I hear a rustle in the bushes behind me I know it is only Windigo looking for pepperoni pizza. And every night I take in the pink plastic flamingos that decorate my front lawn just in case Mary Harris, the famous flamingo thief, decides to kidnap my flock.

In my mind this Horton Bay is real, it is now and it is forever.

Ted Walker, July, 1996
Horton Bay, Michigan

18

Chapter One
Horton Bay Tours, Ltd.

It was a dark and stormy night in Horton Bay.

The early summer heat had begun to cool and most of the good village people had been asleep for hours. Horton Bay is a vibrant metropolis that benefits from industry, commerce and a lucrative tourist trade. The downtown area is dominated by the ruins of the Horton Bay Technology School. The building once covered an entire city block. All that remains today are the huge three story tall columns that had supported the building's gracious portico. The building was destroyed by fire many years ago. The columns are all that were saved. Authorities speculate that the fire was started when a professor was showing students how to change a light bulb. The Horton Bay City Council left the columns as an honor to all the many plumbers and electricians who received their training and degrees from this fine institution. It made little difference to the City Council that several years after the school burned an investigative reporter for The Horton Bay Gazette disclosed that for a mere $5.95, plus shipping and handling, a student could receive a plumber's degree simply by taking a phony correspondence course. Today this scam has pretty much been forgotten and on any given sunny day a person can see lovers seated on the grass in front of the tall, white columns. Picnickers loll about, framed by the column's majestic beauty. It has even become a rite of passage for Horton Bay teenagers to take off their clothes and have their pictures taken in front of the columns. This isn't something that is done secretly, but rather, parents proudly display these pictures on living room walls as proof that their children have come of age. It is considered the greatest honor of all for a person to lose their virginity at the columns' base. Sometimes, there are even pictures of this event, though these pictures normally don't make it to the living room walls. Bonnie Perverd, a local in Horton Bay, did send in one of her pictures to the lurid tabloid, *Porno in the Bay*, and it was published. Bonnie was an overnight sensation and quickly became one of the most popular girls in the bay.

The suburban neighborhoods are comprised of neat, whitewashed cottages that reflect the Northern Michigan summer colony tradition of architecture. For the most part the cottages look pretty much the same, trimmed with dark green shutters, wide front porches, and deeply pitched roofs, with a few traces of Victorian lattice work around the gables. The town stands on a brow of land above Lake Charlevoix, and from downtown Horton Bay the water is always quite visible, deep blue and undulating. The sky is always the same deep blue, and world famous meteorologists have long since concluded that Horton Bay enjoys the best weather in Michigan. Balmy breezes keep the village folk cool on a hot August day while people in Charlevoix and Boyne City swelter and are forced to sit in front of window fans, moping their faces with a wet wash cloth. In January when other people are digging out of a severe winter storm the honest, God fearing people of Horton Bay might be sunbathing on their back deck. It rarely rains in Horton Bay during the day. The village uniquely receives her moisture during the middle of the night while the town slumbers. The night rain is cool in the summer and warm in the winter. It is always refreshing. The foliage is lush, the same color as the dark green cottage shutters. The thick forests that ring the area are filled with mosquito plants, a plant that naturally repels the pesky insects. While the rest of the country is frantically waving their hands in the air and slapping at bugs, the people in Horton Bay are able to enjoy their summers, their picnics, their days at the beach in peace. Horton Bay is a good place to live and most people go to bed at night with a contented smile on their lips.

This particular night a heavy rain pelted Harvey Whippleman's thin porch roof, and down the hill from his house the big waves rolled into the bay from Lake Charlevoix, breaking with the sound of a harangue on the beach where the old sawmill had once stood. Every few minutes a brilliant flash of lightning would momentarily light the black sky. Gusts of wind blew through the tall cedar trees that rim the road to the water. The wind carried the shrill call of a frightened night bird.

Harvey Whippleman, an assistant to the Assistant Deputy Constable, stood on his small, screened in porch watching the summer storm. It was approximately 2:00 a.m. and except for the sound of the storm the village was very quiet. Harvey was the great, great grandson of Three Fingers Holandaze the founder of what is now called Horton Bay. It was only natural that the good people of the village would honor him by making him the assistant to the Assistant Deputy Constable, but the responsibility was enormous and lately he had not been able to sleep at night. Further complicating the matter were Harvey's financial problems. He was flat broke and a huge stack of bills were unpaid and gathering dust on the front hall table. Harvey's prospects appeared dim. Now his job was in jeopardy. Recently, the Constable had put him on double secret probation for exceeding the three hour nap limit per eight hour shift. Harvey knew that double secret probation usually was the final straw so he desperately needed a new way to make some money. Fast money. He normally did his best thinking in the middle of the night . This particular night he was sipping a vodka on the rocks and studying the cottage, which stood about one hundred yards across the road, and was supposed to be unoccupied. He thought that he had seen a solitary figure standing in the upstairs bedroom window. Harvey was edgy. Horton Bay had recently seen an alarming increase in crime. A year earlier the constable had only received one call and that was for a barking dog. This particular year he already had received three calls (though two were for the same barking dog)! The city council was up in arms. Being at the bottom of Horton Bay's law enforcement bureaucracy, Harvey had been called to task at the last council meeting.

Harvey often moonlighted as a spontaneous human combustion investigator, which means that whenever a person mysteriously bursts into flames in Horton Bay Harvey investigates the phenomenon. He first got the idea for this profession from one of those lurid grocery store tabloids that ran a story about a person in Boyne City suddenly bursting into flames, reducing the body to a heap of smoldering ashes. In that incident Harvey sprang into action, hitchhiking to the scene, interviewing witnesses and

21

taking pictures of a charred recliner and the pile of ashes on the seat. He then filed a report with the Horton Bay magazine, *Strange Happenings in the Bay*. Since not too many people burst into flames the Horton Bay City Council felt that Harvey had the time to head up the new crime task force that he had been talking about on the front porch of the General Store.

Harvey opened the screen door and walked outside into the rain. His spindly, knobby kneed legs shook with fear. The rain soaked his curly blond hair making him look like a sickly Harpo Marx. He peered intently at the cottage. And then there, in the upstairs window, he saw a candle burning and the silhouettes of two people. Harvey's heart beat wildly. There were intruders in the bay! He couldn't make out the faces, but something in his gut told him that it was probably the Hokum twins. The boys were identical twins, who had a long history of causing trouble in Horton Bay. When Evelyn Chetum (her father was the respected Horton Bay lawyer with the firm Dewey, Chetum and Howe) first learned that she was to have a baby, she and her live in lover, Herman Hokum, had decided, after many arguments, to name the child Pete if it was a boy and Petunia if a girl. They had no idea that identical twin boys would be born. To solve the problem the first born was named Pete and the second was named Re-Pete.

The Horton Bay constable had a rap sheet on Pete and Re-Pete that would stretch from the General Store to the new Horton Bay Civic Pride Auditorium, which being in the suburbs was about one hundred yards away.

The first recorded crime attributed to Pete and Re-Pete was for littering. The Red Fox Inn had placed a 911 call (the new 911 system had recently replaced the Constable's carrier pigeon service, which an old study conducted by the Horton Bay Institute of Technology had deemed to be antiquated) to the Constable's office. Somebody had thrown a cherry pop can on their front lawn. After questioning the usual suspects and shaking down the village snitch the Constable learned that Pete and Re-Pete had been spotted with red rings around their mouths. Further investigation disclosed that they had bought a can of cherry pop at the General Store. The twins were hustled into the station house for questioning. After several hours of intense interrogation they confessed to the crime. They were sentenced to eight hours of picking up litter on Horton Bay's Magnificent Mile Beach, the beach that *Muscle Magazine* voted one of the top ten beaches in the world. After an hour of scouring the beach Pete and Re-Pete had only found one cigarette butt and because the Constable had hopes of catching an afternoon nap he dismissed the sentence.

Some of the town's people felt that the Constable had been far too lenient. These feelings lasted through the year and into the next when the Constable was running for re-election. In an attempt to win votes the Constable picked Pete and Re-Pete up for jay walking in front of the General Store. The twins were dispatched through Horton Bay's court system (at the time the Constable was also the village judge, having been appointed to a three year term by the mayor) and sentenced to one day in the new, state of the art, Horton Bay Correctional Facility.

It didn't take long for Pete and Re-Pete to tunnel out. They hurriedly dug a two mile tunnel, which ended up exactly underneath the kitchen of Polly Hamhock's house. When Pete and Re-Pete broke through the floor they immediately spotted ten of Polly's freshly baked blueberry pies cooling on the window sill. The boys hadn't eaten for a couple of hours so they sat down at the table and ate all ten pies. What happened next has been widely disputed. What is known is that Mrs. Hamhock put a load of buckshot in the twin's rear ends as they raced for the sanctuary of the Horton Bay swamp where they knew not even the bravest soul would follow them.

Mrs. Hamhock insisted that she shot the boys because they had eaten her pies. Others have speculated that she was merely evening an old score. Everyone in town knew that when the boys were younger they used to follow Polly's only daughter, Margaret, home from Horton Bay High. The twins pronounced the girl's name as though it was spelled Margareet, and they chanted:

Margareet, go wash your feet,
The Health Department is down the street.

Margareet, Margareet,
You've got big, foul smelling feet.

Your Mama's perfume may smell sweet,
So why not splash some on your dumb ol' feet.

Scrub them up and make them shine,
For that bad a smell use turpentine.

Sitting in class you think you're so cool,
Don't you know you're stinking up the school?

I wish I may, I wish I might
Not dream about your smelly feet tonight.

Margaret's mother often vowed that one day she would get Pete and Re-Pete back for this injustice. Most people in the bay simply felt that the spray of bird shot was the twin's payback.

The twins never reappeared. They seemingly were swallowed up in the black abyss of Horton Bay swamp. Over the years Pete and Re-Pete became somewhat of a legend and local folk heroes. Many believed that they were still hiding out in the swamp, calmly waiting for the constable's term to end. Stories were told late at night around many a camp fire. Every summer there were reported sightings with people claiming that they had seen the twins howling at the moon or taking a late night swim with Elvis. Signs were posted in the bay that read, "We love you Pete and Re-Pete" and, "Come back twins, all is forgiven". A local gypsy, Madam Margo and Her All Seeing Glass Eye, once held a seance where she claimed Pete and Re-Pete spoke to her. According to Margo, the twins said they would not return to Horton Bay until the Hamhocks left town. Indeed Polly Hamhock and Margaret moved to East Jordan where they insisted the residents liked the smell of Margaret's feet.

Now as Harvey stared at the two figures in the window he had a marvelous idea. If Pete and Re-Pete had returned to Horton Bay just quite possibly there was a way to make some money on their celebrity status.

One of Harvey's recent money making schemes had been to open a business, which he called Horton Bay Tours, Ltd. The business would charge tourists (commonly called fudgies for their penchant to patronize Horton Bay's one hundred four fudge shops, located in the somewhat seedy, albeit sweet smelling, Fudge Alley district) for an inside look at the many attractions the bay had to offer. Who wouldn't pay big money to hear the twin's story first hand? Harvey's mind worked quickly. Pete and Re-Pete could actually put on a play of sorts, recreating their harrowing experience of being picked up and jailed for jay walking, tunneling to freedom, shot in the butt by Polly Hamhock (who the mayor would try to get to play herself), and hiding out in the swamp for years until a new, more lenient constable was elected. There was enough drama here for at least a five or even six minute play. Why, the mayor calculated, fudgies would probably ante up as much as twenty five dollars a head to see such a show!

Harvey stumbled through the misty rain shouting, "Pete, Re-Pete, at last you've come home! It's me, Harvey Whippleman."

Harvey rushed into the cottage and bounded up the stairs towards

24

the room where he had seen the twins. The door was closed, but through the keyhole he could see the faint glow of candlelight. He hesitated for a moment and then bent down, pressing his eye to the keyhole. Best not to startle Pete and Re-Pete. After all, living in the Horton Bay swamp may have turned them into wild animals (which he secretly hoped was the case since that would improve the show).

Harvey squinted through the keyhole, his eye darting about the dimly lit room. All at once he felt his heart leap into his throat. Sitting at a small writing table was none other than famed Nobel prize winner, Ernest Hemingway! Harvey stared in disbelief. Hemingway had been dead for years, yet there he sat. My God, Harvey rationalized, it must be Hemingway's ghost. And then the other figure appeared. It was Claud Balls, the writer who wrote the famous Horton Bay novel, *The Tiger's Revenge*, and then developed a taste for cheap wine. Within a year Claud was Horton Bay's town drunk, consuming vast quantities of Thunder Bird (What's the word? Thunder Bird! Say it twice, it's awfully nice! Drink it up 'cause, it's cheap at twice the price). After he began hitting the booze he spoke in a very distinctive style of short, to the point sentences like, "yup," and, "nope" and, "shut up, ya bum, or I'll knock your block off." Rumor had it in Horton Bay that it was Claud who taught the young Hemingway how to write, using the hard boiled dialogue that later made Hemingway famous.

Harvey was about to open the door when he heard Claud say, "For the last time Ernest, you must learn to say what you mean, mean what you say and be ready to back it up." So it was true, Harvey realized. Hemingway did learn how to write from his days in Horton Bay. This story would undoubtedly make a better attraction for the fledgling Horton Bay Tours, Ltd. than the Pete and Re-Pete play. Harvey realized that he had no experience talking with ghosts so he quickly slipped out of the house and returned to his screened in porch and the vodka on the rocks. He sat down in his favorite chair and breathed a sigh of relief. For the first time he truly felt that his Horton Bay Tours, Ltd. venture would be a success.

The next afternoon when he got out of bed Harvey contacted Madam Margo and Her All Seeing Glass Eye. During the night, about the time he was sipping his eighth vodka, he had come to the conclusion that he had very little previous experience with the after life and that he needed a true professional to negotiate a contract with the two ghosts. Madam Margo, a savvy businesswoman, demanded a piece of the action. She quickly cut herself in for a fifty one percent ownership in Horton Bay Tours, Ltd. Harvey could care less. He knew that forty nine percent of a dynamic Horton Bay Tours, Ltd. would provide enough money to boost his lifestyle considerably.

Madam Margo wasted no time in signing both ghosts up for an eight week summer run. The contract called for Hemingway to sit at the window pretending to write the great American novel. Claud Balls would stand over him hollering, "Just write one true sentence, Ernie!"

And after pondering the order for a moment Ernest would shout, "the trout was hooked and he knew it."

"No, Ernie, be more to the point!"

At this juncture Ernest would stand up and yell, "It was a good and wonderful trout and he was brave to die in such a fight. Truly."

"Good, Ernie, very good," Claud would say, approvingly.

Then both ghosts would stand and wave out the window to the to the assembled crowd. The show was an enormous success and was sold out every night that first summer. Fortified with this good fortune Horton Bay Tours, Ltd. raised the admission fee for the next summer season to thirty five dollars per person with no break for children under twelve. The second summer the business also added several new attractions.

The world loves success and prosperity. Horton Bay is no exception. The village wasted no time in distinguishing Harvey by voting him in as mayor. Madam Margo and Her All Seeing Glass Eye retired to Las Vegas with the promise that every month Harvey would send her share of the Horton Bay Tours, Ltd. profits. The first month Harvey considered "cooking the books" and sending Madam Margo a reduced share of the money, but he was frightened to death of that All Seeing Glass Eye. So every month he dutifully sent the correct sum of the burgeoning profits, which Madam Margo promptly lost at the Black Jack table, her All Seeing Glass Eye somehow failing to see the dealer's hand.

The second summer an emergency advisory from Horton Bay Animal Control (HAC) gave Harvey another idea for the business. HAC had issued a snake advisory for the greater Horton Bay area. Apparently, Oscar Meyer's pet snakes were missing. The serpents were non poisonous and posed no real threat to humans, but for political reasons HAC was taking no chances and issued the alert. The tropical snakes escaped when Oscar's cleaning lady accidentally left the doors of the ninety two reptile cages open. The snakes escaped to the outdoors through a ventilation shaft and hurriedly slithered off in several different directions. HAC warned that these snakes will travel great distances in search of food, especially during the daylight hours on warm, sunny days. What particularly disturbed the citizens, however, was the advisory's notification that the snakes most likely would seek shelter indoors during the cooler, evening hours. People were warned to keep all doors closed. This precaution included houses, garages, sheds and outhouses. The official advisory was posted at the General Store and included the following advice:

1) Do not move quickly! Very cautiously put as much distance between yourself and the snake(s) as possible.
2) As you retreat look the viper(s) directly in the eyes.
3) DO NOT turn your back on the serpent(s) as this encourages aggressive behavior.

4) Check all toilet bowls before using as these snakes have been known to enter sewer and septic lines when searching for food.

5) Keep all house pets smaller than fifty pounds in-doors until the snake advisory has officially been lifted.

6) If a viper(s) is spotted immediately call HAC and a trained snake professional will be dispatched.

The public panicked. People sat up at night with nets, homemade traps and weapons of destruction. They poured and lit rings of gasoline around their houses in hopes that this would block the creatures assault. The one bright result of the snakes being loose in the bay was the report from Horton Bay Rodent Control that the mouse and rat populations were markedly down that summer. One local resident, a certain Johnny Slick, even went so far as to train his dog Bingo to track snakes. Bingo was trained daily for several hours at a time. He was taught to pick up the scent, to track, to stalk his prey and then to pounce in for the kill. Bingo loved his work and learned quickly.

When Harvey Whippleman first saw Bingo in action the idea for another Horton Bay Tours, Ltd. attraction struck like a bolt of lightning. Why not charge fudgies for the excitement of a lifetime of spending a day in the Horton Bay swamps with Bingo, the snake hunting dog? Harvey figured that fudgies would gladly ante up fifty dollars an hour to thrill to the hunt. The hunters would trudge through the sludge, alert, watching Bingo in action. Bingo would be further trained to either kill the snake or hold it for capture. The fudgie would control the action through voice commands. When the fudgie yells, "eat, Bingo, eat!" the snake is a goner, but should the fudgie decide to take a pet home then he would shout, "subdue, Bingo, subdue." Bingo would then grip the snake behind the head and apply enough pressure to close off the snake's windpipe. Once the snake was rendered unconscious a tour representative would drop it into a gunny sack. Once all three hundred of Oscar Meyer's snakes were captured the tour would focus on the headwaters of Horton Creek where the elusive Horton Bay Cobra makes its home. Harvey was beside himself with anticipation.

Bingo, the snake hunting dog proved to be a bonanza for Horton Bay Tours, Ltd. The money rolled in as men, women and children flocked to Horton Bay for snake hunts. Harvey became so intrigued with this attraction that he took to wearing a pith helmet and safari jacket when he sold the Bingo keepsakes that the merchandising arm of Horton Bay Tours, Ltd. created. The real money, however, resulted with the production of the Bingo action video, which sold for $89.95 plus shipping and handling.

One of the first things that Harvey discovered, once the hunts penetrated the dark swamp, was that Pete and Re-Pete actually had spent very little time there. Harvey calculated from an empty can of Spam that the twins had simply passed through the swamp on their way to Mancelona where it was later learned that they took a job at the Sunny Disposition Diner as singing waiters. The boys had beautiful voices and, as good fortune would have it, when a talent scout for Happy Times Radio happened to be vacationing in Mancelona the twins were "discovered." They quickly signed contracts and headed for Hollywood where they found success with a two person drama, which they wrote and starred in called, *The Monkey's Dream*. This play poignantly chronicled Tarzan's and Cheeta's quest to immigrate to America. At each night's sold out performance the boys took turns playing Cheeta, the most popular role. Sadly, the act ended abruptly when Re-Pete fell in love with a belly dancer, who worked at the Kit Kat Club in West Los Angeles. The dancer was part of a sibling act called the Swinging VaVoom Sisters, Rita, Stella and VaVa. Re-Pete fell head over heels for VaVa VaVoom. The two moved to Honolulu when they learned that Eddie's Pirate Bar was looking for a replacement for its main attraction, Wanda Lust and her Fifty Thousand Dollar Treasure Chest. Apparently, the fifty nine year old Wanda had taken ill with diarrhea (Wanda politely called it "the back door boogie") after eating a record nineteen bowls of chili at Shorty's Chili Parlor, whose motto was, "We guarantee to give you enough gas to drive around the island."

Pete gamely tried to struggle on with the act. He refused to take on a new partner and played both parts for one month before being admitted to the Pleasantville Mental Institute for observation. Rita and Stella moved to Wichita, Kansas where they taught belly dancing at the local senior citizens home. Years later, Harvey Whippleman and Horton Bay Tours, Ltd. booked Re-Pete and VaVa at the Horton Bay Playhouse where they resurrected, *The Monkey's Dream*, with the part of Tarzan being played by the muscular VaVa.

Over the years Horton Bay Tours, Ltd. continued to flourish. Harvey continued to operate the business out of his home, which the locals now referred to as Action Central. Every year Harvey added more attractions and the money continued to pour in. Within three years Horton Bay Tours, Ltd. had earned a ranking in the Fortune 500. Times were good, life was good. As the mayor of Horton Bay and CEO of Horton Bay Tours, Ltd. Harvey was in a position of leadership and power. He had indeed come a long way from his childhood in Horton Bay where he grew up on Skid Road, the poorest section in town. As frequently happens to people in this position Harvey soon began to dream of building a new Horton Bay upon which everything would have his signature. There would be a new 90,000 seat domed stadium and an NFL football team. The stadium would be named Whippleman Stadium and the team would be called the Whipplettes. There would be a Whippleman Mall, a Whippleman Ciné Four, the Whippleman Library, a Whippleman City Park with a statue of himself and maybe even a new outhouse called the Whippleman Privy, and if it weren't for Madam Margo and Her All Seeing Glass Eye he'd probably rename the business Whippleman Productions, Inc. That would come later, but he knew that for now he had to be careful about thinking such thoughts because of that damn all seeing glass eye.

The Horton Bay General Store is the town's gathering place. Every morning people pay fifty cents for unlimited coffee and conversation. Harvey spent most of his mornings in bed, but occasionally he rose early and joined the others at the General Store. He generally consumed seven or eight cups of coffee and lately had started to complain about the price.

One morning, in protest to the fifty cents all you can drink policy, he wandered down to a friend's shack on Skid Road. The friend's name was Lunch Meat, a name bestowed upon him by locals because he always ate bologna, pickle loaf, ham or any other cold cut that happened to be on sale. Lunch Meat had been married once (the marriage only lasted nine days, or as some have speculated, just long enough for his wife to get tired of cold cuts). The wedding reception, however, had been a huge success

29

that was talked about in Horton Bay for years. The Horton Bay Gazette quoted one happy guest as gushing, "My word! There must have been at least a dozen different types of lunch meat on the buffet table!" That's when the name Lunch Meat was bestowed. Most people in Horton Bay forgot his real name. He simply became Lunch Meat.

Lunch Meat was a sallow faced wharf rat who claimed to have been abducted twenty seven times by space aliens. He also had spent several years traveling on the lecture circuit. For awhile he had been booked at many of the country's most prestigious colleges presenting his theory that eternity is always one second longer than tomorrow. He now spent most of his time trying to snap a picture of Hortie, the Hortness Monster. Lunch Meat believed that if he could just get one or two good pictures from the camera he'd found at the dump (now renamed the Whippleman Refuse Center) he could strike it rich by selling them to The Horton Bay Gazette.

Harvey liked visiting Lunch Meat every now and then. This particular morning when Lunch Meat offered him a cup of coffee and a wedge of head cheese Harvey noticed that Lunch Meat was heating each cup of water with one of those heating elements that are designed to hang onto the lip of the cup. The element heated the water to nearly boiling and then Lunch Meat moved the element to the next cup of water and stirred a teaspoon of instant coffee into the first. Harvey watched this procedure with fascination. Suddenly he had yet another idea for Horton Bay Tours, Ltd. This idea would prove to be the one that made Harvey and the company internationally famous.

Harvey figured that if one heating element would heat a cup of water then ten thousand heating elements would surely heat the winter water in Horton Bay. That would turn the Magnificent Mile Beach into a year round attraction. Fudgies would flock to the warm water for their winter vacations, and fudgies meant more business for the company. Harvey also calculated that he could purchase the winter swimming rights to the bay and charge customers at least seventy five dollars a head for the privilege of taking a winter swim in the bay. An additional benefit of year round warm water in the bay would be that Harvey could now open the Horton Bay Octopus Park that had been on the drawing table for the last three years.

That afternoon Harvey ordered ten thousand coffee cup heating elements from the Horton Bay Water Heating Company, which was at the time, and still is, the largest manufacturer of coffee cup heating elements in the world. Harvey then held a town meeting and introduced his plan to the good people of the village. He exalted the benefits of turning Horton Bay into a year round vacation spot. He sold the populace on the idea that more tourists meant a better economy and that a better economy meant more money in their pockets. What Harvey was really trying to sell them on, however, was the idea that each house in Horton Bay run extension cords down to the bay and provide power for a minimum of thirty plug ins for the heating elements. Harvey had already figured that the electric bill from the new Whippleman Power Plant would be astronomical. One heckler in the crowd shouted, "What this really means is more money in your pocket, Harvey!" Harvey immediately had the Constable escort the heckler (who happened to be his mother) from the auditorium. Once order was restored, a secret ballot vote was taken. After pretending to count the ballots in a back room Harvey announced that beginning the Tuesday following Labor Day everyone was to plug in their extension cords and strategically place their thirty heating elements in the water.

Sure enough, Harvey's idea worked. On Christmas day the water temperature in Horton Bay was recorded at a pleasant seventy eight degrees. Tourists swarmed into the village filling every available hotel and motel room. The Magnificent Mile Beach was packed with happy bathers, who luxuriated in the warm water. Harvey erected huge sun lamps that augmented the weak winter light. His Horton Bay Tours, Ltd. concession stand sold tube upon tube of sun screen, beach towels and cotton candy. The most popular concession proved to be hand dipped ice cream cones that Horton Bay Tours, Ltd sold for nine dollars apiece. The fudgies loved ice cream and before long the winter tourists became known not as fudgies, but as cone suckers. The money continued to roll in. Harvey was becoming one of the wealthiest men in America. He even considered running for President of the United States representing his newly formed Hortonian Party.

For the time being though he turned his attention to the Octopus Park. Located where Horton Creek flows into the bay the Octopus Park was flanked by bleacher seats that could accommodate 16,000 people. An enormous artificial reef was built. Special octopus cages were constructed. Finally, twenty two wild octopuses were netted in Horton Bay and installed inside the reef. The octopuses underwent hours of rigorous training until Harvey at last pronounced them ready to perform. Crowds jammed the bleacher seats to capacity, anxiously watching the octopuses leap repeatedly out of the water through hoops. One special attraction was the feeding, which cost an additional twenty dollars to view. The Horton Bay Animal Guild at first opposed this spectacle, but later relented, insisting that young children, vegetarians, people with queasy stomachs or bad

31

hearts not be allowed to watch the octopus feed. Another special attraction occurred at every one of the ten daily shows when one of the trainers would randomly select a participant from the audience. The participant would then stand on a dock and one of the large male octopus would surface, approach and finally embrace the participant with all nine tentacles. Occasionally, an obstreperous octopus would jerk the screaming participant off the dock and drag the body out to open water. For awhile, Harvey considered discontinuing this part of the show, but decided to leave it in after he saw the tremendous ovation it received whenever the trainer was unable to recover a participant. The next part of the show (and one that cost an additional twenty five dollars) allowed participants to don scuba gear and enter special octopus cages. The cages would then be lowered into the water and the customers could view the octopuses performing in their natural environment. After the first week Harvey was forced to limit this attraction to people who weighed more than two hundred fifty pounds, or as one octopus trainer put it, "You must be big enough so that it would be extremely difficult for you to be yanked though the bars of the cage."

Even bad luck, or in this case, bad publicity, seemed to work in Harvey's favor. The Horton Bay Fly Fishing Association began to bitterly complain that the warm water in the bay was driving the Saber Tooth salmon into Horton Creek. The vicious Saber Tooth salmon was wreaking havoc with the Brook trout, not to mention anglers legs. The association wrote nasty letters to the editor for publication in The Horton Bay Gazette, they picketed the Octopus Park and even went on a bathing strike, vowing not to shower until a grievous wrong was righted. Since Harvey lived downwind from several protesters he finally relented and in a munificent show of good will announced that he would lease the headwater of Horton Creek to the association for the pittance of only fifty thousand dollars a year. The headwater was a good five miles from the Octopus park and therefore the water was unaffected by the heating elements and remained cold, which provided an ideal mating ground for the Saber Tooth salmon. Everyone left the bargaining table happy.

The Horton Bay environmentalists were not so easily placated when Harvey entered into an oil drilling project with Salvatore (The Salamander) LaBianca. The Salamander was most notably known for being the only student to be thrown out of the Horton Bay Theological Seminary. During his final year, and following a lengthy investigation, the Board of Regents voted unanimously to expel The Salamander for cheating on his thesis, which he had tentatively titled, THE VATICAN:

32

CONTROLLED BY THE POPE OR THE MAFIA?

Following his expulsion The Salamander drifted around Horton Bay looking for something to do with himself. He spent hour upon hour staring at the sky and people in the bay began whispering that he was touched in the head. Indeed, he did seem confused. For one thing, he was always mixing up holidays. One Christmas he handed out Easter baskets for presents. He had filled the baskets with decorated eggs, but he had forgotten to hard boil the eggs. It was only a matter of minutes before the neighborhood children discovered this oversight and began lobbing raw eggs at passing cars. Brendon LaBlance, the Horton Bay Fire Chief was called to hose down the cars. Meanwhile, the Constable found The Salamander, dressed as a leprechaun, sitting in a tree behind the General Store celebrating Saint Patrick's Day.

The next spring when The Salamander appeared at a town council meeting with the announcement that his geological surveys had revealed vast fields of synthetic oil beneath the water in Horton Bay he was laughed out of the meeting. As luck would have it, Harvey Whippleman was just coming off a tremendously successful year with Horton Bay Tours, Ltd. His accountant had recently confirmed that a huge tax payment would be necessary. Harvey decided to use The Salamander's claim that there was synthetic oil beneath the bay as an excuse to build a huge platform in the bay. Harvey knew that a platform would be necessary if he was to expand the Octopus Park. He would build the platform under the guise of drilling for oil, and then when no oil was discovered he could take the cost as a loss on his taxes. Harvey had become quite crafty.

Six months later Harvey was sitting on his porch drinking a vodka on the rocks when he heard a tremendous whooshing roar from the bay, which sounded much like the deafening thunder of the one thousand foot Horton Bay Falls. This was followed by raucous screams of delight. A few moments later The Salamander rushed up the hill from the bay and burst onto the porch. He was covered in oil and only his eyes and mouth showed white. They had struck oil! And it was the mother lode!

The Horton Bay Environmental Society immediately grew concerned. They were worried about oil spills in the bay. To thwart drilling operations the society set up a boat blockade. Unafraid, they would position themselves between the oil well and Harvey's new super tanker. Harvey, concerned about possible law suits should a collision occur, petitioned the City Council to provide an escort for his tanker (named The Salamander I). Harvey, as mayor, used a little known provision in the city charter that stated that the village of Horton Bay, if ever it deemed necessary, would form a Coast Guard to patrol the bay. Harvey claimed that a patrol was now necessary and thereby sought city funds to protect and escort The Salamander I. The Horton Bay Environmental Society brought a great deal of pressure to bear on the City Council. The society's president played pinochle every Saturday night with Chicky Symthe, who was the City Superintendent. Gorey Goralnik, the society's Anti Pollution Captain, spent Sunday afternoons with the Amazing Waldo, who was the Council Secretary. Gorey and the Amazing Waldo were in charge of seeing how many people could squeeze into the phone booth that stood at the foot of the General Store front porch. This group of septuagenarians was an extremely close group and so Gorey was able to enlist the Amazing Waldo's support in fighting Harvey's plan to use city funds to protect the Salamander I.

When the City Council voted down the motion for a Horton Bay Coast Guard Harvey hit upon another idea. He remembered Fire Chief LaBlance's complaint that too many illegal immigrants from East Jordan had been slipping across the Horton Bay border in order to take advantage of some of the village's many citizen benefits, such as free cotton candy for all adults on Friday afternoons. Many were sneaking into town under the cover of darkness across the bay. The City Council tossed the problem back into Chief LaBlance's face and assigned him the additional duty of curtailing these border crossings. The council issued a statement that, "Our borders have simply become too porous! Something has got to be done. It used to be that all we had to worry about was a couple from Grand Rapids or a family of four from Grosse Point sneaking into town every now and then. Now we have hundreds of East Jordanians and Boyne City people trying to illegally immigrate to Horton Bay!".

Fire Chief LaBlance insisted that his elite fire and rescue team was already overworked and also committed to a specialized training course that he promised would put his crack squad on the cutting edge of technology. His team had just completed ten weeks of advanced training in coping with anglers who, distraught over not catching their limit of Saber Tooth salmon, threatened to jump off the Horton Creek bridge. These "bridge leapers" as Chief LaBlance called them were beginning to pose a problem for his staff. He reported that the special training had been necessary because his team often had to cope with Horton Bay residents, who by their own admission said that they loved nothing better than a good bridge jump. Often crowds would gather and taunt the bridge leaper with shouts of, "Chicken!" and, "Bet you won't do it!".

Fire Chief LaBlance stated that this training plus the proposed nuclear preparedness drills that would be held over the next several weeks would leave his squad unavailable for border patrol duties. He argued that the near melt down of the Horton Bay nuclear reactor should be his first priority. Accordingly, he had already planned a test for his squad that would consist of a "mock melt down". Chief LaBlance had secretly made arrangements for a local trouble maker (nick named the Powder Monkey because of his interest in dynamite) to sneak into the nuclear power facility. The Powder Monkey would then heat the core to an exceedingly dangerous level. Chief LaBlance would then sound the alarm and grade his troops on their response. During the most recent near melt down he was quite disturbed to learn that over ninety percent of his squad was smelt fishing and unavailable.

While this debate raged through the bay a group of Horton Bay toughs had started a game they called, Toss the Fudgie. The game consisted of using an abandoned ice cream cone lure to snare an illegal fudgie, carrying him to the city limits and seeing how far they could toss the hapless individual. The record stood at thirty two feet. Every night down at the Eager Beaver Tavern bets were wagered as to whether the so called invincible forty foot barrier would ever be broken.

The situation was rapidly getting out of hand. Harvey used the fact that one fudgie toss that seemingly did break the forty foot barrier was disqualified because it had been wind aided as justification to allocate emergency funds for the Coast Guard. Then a black market business began issuing phoney local and native documents to the illegal immigrants. For twenty five measly bucks someone from East Jordan could be outfitted with papers that passed him off as a bonafide Hortonian. Normally a person had to live in the village for forty five years to be called a local. For thirty bucks a person could purchase papers that stated he was a native!

Harvey used civic pride and the illegal gaming on the Toss the Fudgie game to bring the Coast Guard proposal up for vote again. This time the motion passed and the City Council inaugurated the Horton Bay Coast Guard, feeling that this remedy would be far cheaper than erecting a fifty foot wall around the bay. The Coast Guard not only put a virtual stop to illegal immigrants crossing the border into Horton Bay, but The Salamander I now had safe escort through the Environmental Society's blockade. Eventually, the society gave up trying to harass oil drilling operations and went back to fighting the construction of the proposed Horton Canal that would link Walloon Lake and Horton Bay. The young toughs went back to watermelon spitting contests, forgetting about their Toss the Fudgie game.

Chapter Two
OUR FOUNDING FATHER

In 1858 Willie Holton escaped from the Minkoff Mental Institution in New York City. He headed west vowing never again to be subjected to the dreaded dripping cold water cure, which was popular at the time for treating people who were addicted to playing leap frog and spin the bottle. The authorities were hot on his trail so Willie cut off the thumb and forefinger of his right hand in order to change his appearance. He then changed his name to Holandaze, which was his mother's maiden name. Three Fingers Holandaze had frequently heard the plaintive plea to "Go west". He figured that he could become lost in the wilderness and then, free of the white jacketed guards at the Minkoff Mental Institute, he could at long last pursue his lifelong dream of opening a taco restaurant. Sitting under the dripping cold water at the institute he had often dreamed about this restaurant. It would be called Taco Heaven and feature fifty different types of tacos.

Three Fingers traveled west eventually entering Michigan and into the area of what is now referred to as, "down state". He felt the down staters were a bit stuffy so he built two canoes, lashed them together, hoisted a sail and launched the craft in Lake Michigan, turning northward. Fellow yachtsmen scoffed at his two canoe rig, but the scoffing soon turned to admiration when they noticed the speed and agility of the boat. Three Fingers named his vessel The Catamaran, after his great grandfather, Louie Catamaran Holandaze. Later, Three fingers would form a ship building company and mass produce his Catamaran sail boat.

Three Fingers sailed north until he reached what is now called Lake

Charlevoix. Sorely in need of provisions he jibed his catamaran and sailed into the Pine River channel where he noticed that the bridge was down. He tacked back and forth in the small channel (in those days it was only ten feet wide) until he at last lost his temper, pursed his lips and gave a long whistle followed by a short. Three Fingers raised one of his fingers and waved at the bridge operator, trying desperately to get his attention. He did, and the operator immediately raised the bridge so that Three Fingers could sail into Round Lake. Tourists who were standing nearby took all this in and it wasn't long before Three Fingers was credited with starting two customs in Charlevoix: A long whistle followed by a short when you wanted the bridge to be opened, and raising your index finger at another person whenever you became angry.

Three fingers thought the ten cent marina fee charged by a local Indian, Chief Quinton, was exorbitant so he sailed east on Lake Charlevoix. Just as the sunlight began to fade he noticed a magnificent bay to his left. The bay was deserted and looked to be a perfect place to spend the night. Three Fingers entered the bay and ended up staying for the next forty seven years of his life.

The Indians on this part of the lake were not friendly so Three Fingers began at once to build a fort. He named his new fort, Fort Itch, in honor of the mosquitos that incessantly had swarmed about him as he labored away. Three Fingers had hired two men who had stumbled into the area, fallen in love with the beautiful bay and decided to stay. They accidently discovered that if you poured sour milk all over your body then the mosquito swarms would stay away. It became a morning ritual for the three men to wallow in pools of sour milk before starting to work on Fort Itch. The Indians marveled at this ingenious discovery, but nonetheless referred to Three Fingers' two helpers as Butter Milk and Stinky. When the supply of milk ran short Three Fingers enlisted the local Indians to high-jack a shipment of heavy cream and yogurt that was headed from Charlevoix to Boyne City. The Indians were caught and ratted out on Three Fingers. The Charlevoix Sheriff sent a wagon and four deputies to arrest Three Fingers, Butter Milk and Stinky. They were immediately arraigned and the trail was set for the next day. That night they planned a daring jail break. They began digging a tunnel. All three men would fill their pockets with dirt and every five minutes ask to use the out house. As they walked to the out house they would empty the dirt from their pockets. The Sheriff began to get suspicious at the number of times the men were using the out house, but Three Fingers convinced him that a bad case of flu had been ravaging the area. By midnight the tunnel was competed. They burrowed upwards and discovered that they had tunneled under Faye's Hamburger Kitchen, a local eatery. Faye was just preparing to close up when she heard a digging sound beneath her floor. She thought that she was being invaded by one or more of those cunning Horton Bay raccoons. Determined to teach the raccoons a lesson she grabbed two of her freshly baked cherry pies and put them directly to the side of the digging sound. She then poured an entire bottle of alum onto the pies. Then she left for the night. About ten minutes later Three Fingers, Butter Milk and Stinky broke though the floor and peered into the diner. They spotted the cherry pies. The tunnel digging had left them famished and they tore into the pies. It only took a couple of seconds for the bitter alum to strike. All three men began spitting out the pie at the same time. Their faces twisted, they let out piercing, anguished cries. They dove back into the tunnel and returned to the Charlevoix Correctional Facility where they knew there was a bucket of lake water. It took over five hours of rinsing their mouths out before they felt back to normal. By this time it was morning and time to go to court.

The first case on the docket was the city versus Roughhouse Williams. Roughhouse was accused of throwing a dead skunk in old lady Hamlet's open bedroom window. Apparently, Roughhouse had a crush on old lady Hamlet and thought that this would be a good way to get her attention. The second case had to do with the Charlevoix mayor being accused of throwing a juke box into the Pine River. Three Fingers, Buttermilk and Stinky were led into the courtroom and seated next to Roughhouse and the mayor. When Judge Gordon entered the courtroom he immediately noticed that swarms of mosquitos were hovering in the air. As the case against Roughhouse progressed more and more mosquitos flew in through the open windows. Everyone inside was busy slapping at mosquitos. Judge Gordon's face and neck quickly became covered with bites. Finally in desperation he called out to the bailiff, "Can't anything be done about these blasted mosquitos?" The bailiff just looked back at the judge in surprise, realizing that this was the first time in two years that the judge had spoken to him. At this juncture Three Fingers jumped up from his seat and asked the judge for a glass of sour milk. The judge, confused by the swarming mosquitos, told an assistant to get the glass of sour milk. When the glass was delivered Three Fingers ran up to the judge and threw the sour milk in the judge's face. "Take that, your honor," he yelled.

"What the hell?" the judge stammered. "Bailiff, restrain this prisoner! Sheriff, arrest this prisoner! Somebody get me a towel!"

"Don't wipe that sour milk off your face, your honor," Three

Fingers shouted.

"And why not?" the judge shouted back, his face dripping with clumps of curdled milk.

"No mosquitos," Three Fingers answered simply. "See, the mosquitos aren't bothering you any more."

The judge looked about him and noticed that the mosquito swarms were avoiding him. He got up and walked toward one of the larger swarms. The mosquitos escaped through the open window. The judge was amazed. He returned to the bench and sat down. Then he motioned for Three Fingers, Buttermilk and Stinky to approach the bench. He commended all three on their effort to rid the courtroom of the mosquitos and then dropped the charge against them of high-jacking the milk wagon. In fact, he hired them to throw sour milk in his face every Tuesday during the summer when court was being held, and whenever there was a jury trial he had them hurl sour milk at the jury.

Three Fingers celebrated his release by throwing a polka party at Fort Itch. He forced the Indians who squealed on him to play the tuba. By all accounts it was quite a party, lasting well into the night. Three Fingers prepared tacos for everybody, which were so well received that the next day he began building his restaurant, Taco Heaven. To this day that restaurant still stands in the same location, though now it is owned by a New York fast food concern called Currentview Amalgamated Industries, Incorporated.

Following that first party at Fort Itch it became a Saturday night tradition to have a polka party. Over the years the tuba playing Indians had become disenchanted with the instrument. They claimed that the oom pah pah beat was slowly driving them insane. They also were a bit upset that they had to perform while the others played cow patty gambling, a game Stinky had invented and which had become very popular in the bay. The game consists of mapping out a series of circles in the cow pasture. The circles vary in size with a higher point level for the smaller the circle. Several well fed cows are then released and given one hour to do their thing. Bets are wagered as to which cow will hit which circle. The gamblers often ring the gaming field cheering the cows on to bigger and better efforts. Even today cow patty gambling is a popular pastime at the exclusive Horton Bay Country Club.

After years and years of enduring the Saturday night polka parties the Indians finally revolted. Three Fingers was by now an old man and had grown quite feeble, especially late at night after polishing off a jug of hard cider. The Indians had a story that had been passed down through the generations of a huge sea monster that lived in the depths of the bay. They now saw their opportunity to put an end to the Saturday night polka parties once and for all. On this particular Saturday night they waited until Three Fingers had consumed his jug of hard cider and worn himself out doing the polka. They then grabbed him and carried him down to the water where they tossed him into the deepest part of the bay. Three Fingers sank like a stone. The Indians at once called upon the sea monster to devour Three Fingers and put an end to their suffering. That was the end of Three Fingers Holandaze He was never seen again.

The next day Stinky and Butter Milk decided they better have a funeral, eat some tacos and have one last polka party in honor of their lost leader. They hired a traveling preacher to perform the bayside service. Butter Milk and Stinky had known for a long time that Three Fingers Holandaze's real name was Willie Holton. They figured that now was the time to bring this out into the open. After all, the Minkoff Mental Institute couldn't touch him now. They hurriedly whispered this information in the preacher's ear. When it came time for the service the preacher (now fortified with some of Three Finger's hard cider) mistakenly kept referring to Three Fingers as, "Our dearly departed, brother Horton". Somehow the name stuck and the next year the Indians began referring to the burgeoning village as Horton's Bay. The newly established newspaper (soon to be named The Horton Bay Gazette) decided to print a story about the new name for the village. The typesetter couldn't find an apostrophe so he called the village Horton Bay for the story.

Three Fingers Holandaze aka Willie Holton aka our dearly departed brother Horton is clearly credited with being the founding father of what is now Horton Bay. His death has perpetrated the stories of the sea monster locals now call Hortie. Taco Heaven offers more than fifty varieties of tacos and sells more tacos than Senorita Peggy's ten roadside taco shacks combined. Three Fingers is also credited with establishing the Horton Bay Mail Order Bride Service that today supplies over ninety percent of the available women in Horton Bay (this business is not to be confused with Fonda Peter's Escort Service, which the Constable shut down after only eight years of being in business). Three Finger's sour milk mosquito remedy became the basis for the Scat Squito bug repellent, which is now sold the world over. He likewise started what has become the world famous Run For The Slop pig races, held every summer in downtown Horton Bay. The race historically attracts some of the fastest pigs in the world and is run on a half mile track that tests the endurance of even the most durable thoroughbred swine. The race boasts three water hazards, four mud wallows and one five foot tall jump. The track also tests the pig's courage with the famous Frying Pan Backstretch. Here the pigs must pass an oversize frying pan in order to reach the finish line. The Run For The Slop pig race generally attracts over one hundred thousand spectators.

Every year nearly everyone of the one hundred thousand spectators journey to the Three Fingers Memorial Park, which is located just east of the bay. There, they gaze in silent admiration at the statue of our founding father. The statue displays Three Fingers holding a jug of hard cider in his left hand. His right hand has the thumb and forefinger missing and is holding a glass of sour milk. He is sitting on a tuba with a smile on his face.

Chapter Three
THE COLLECTION

Harvey Whippleman loved to stop at Taco Heaven every afternoon for a snack. He especially loved the Big Horton, which was a triple bean burrito with extra jalapeños.

It was Saturday afternoon and Harvey was hurrying to get to Horton Bay High for the graduation ceremony of Snooty Peterson's boy. Harvey hadn't had any lunch and was famished. He figured that he could breeze through the Taco Heaven drive thru, pick up a Big Horton, eat in the car and still make it to the school on time. He decided to splurge and bought two Big Hortons, gobbling both down in a matter of a few minutes.

He was standing in the hallway with a small clutch of family friends and relatives waiting for the principal to show up when he felt the first stirring in the pit of his belly. He felt the familiar swelling, a bloating, begin to extend his stomach. He was having a gas attack! A bad one! He tightened his buttocks, squeezing as he tried to stem the growing pressure.

He tried to think about something other than the gas pocket that seemed to swell by the second. The pain intensified as it began to creep around to the small of his back. He fought to control himself. He was barely able to shake the principal's hand when he arrived for fear that a moments loss of concentration would result in a loss of control.

The principal asked everyone to move to the front of the gym. Harvey had to waddle straight legged down the aisle as he struggled to control the balloon of bean burrito gas that had now traveled southward from the small of his back to the crack of his butt, and threatened to explode at any moment. The gas pocket shuddered as Harvey walked. It trembled and rumbled ominously much as a steaming, simmering volcano gives a warning before the big blast. Harvey fought with all his might to suppress the final eruption. He smiled nervously at the principal's wife, who greeted him, "It's such a pleasure to have you here today, Mr. Mayor."

The principal had just introduced the class valedictorian when the thundering blast took place. The huge explosion of gas boomed with such terrifying ferocity that the glass windows rattled and shook violently. The basketball backboard at the near end of the gym vibrated as though slam dunked by some invisible hand. It was later reported that dishes toppled from the shelves in the cafeteria next door to the gym. A baby boy howled in sudden fear while everyone else, shaken from the booming roar, turned and glared at Harvey. In a matter of seconds the area had filled with a noxious odor and the entire group was forced to retreat through the rear door to the back lawn. Eyes watered, skin burned and people groped for handkerchiefs to press to their noses. Women cried out in fear. Men struggled, gasping for fresh air. Students laughed and bolted for freedom. The school secretary put in a 911 call and Fire Chief LaBlance was summoned at the Town House Bar. He and his troops arrived in full antibacterial rubber suits that covered their entire bodies. They wore small oxygen tanks on their backs and blindly groped through the lime green fog that hung inside the gym. Fire Chief LaBlance brought in large fans to clear the air. Snooty Peterson and the principal were forced to ask Harvey to leave. Fire Chief LaBlance threatened to turn the entire matter over to the Constable for investigation.

Harvey was so embarrassed and infuriated when he got back to his house that he immediately called Taco Heaven and asked for the manager. Now most people in Horton Bay are somewhat in awe of Harvey because he is mayor and because of all the money he has made with Horton Bay Tours, Ltd., but the Taco Heaven manager was not to be intimidated.

Perhaps this was because he wasn't originally from the village. He had been brought in by Taco World, a division of Currentview Amalgamated Industries, Incorporated and like many outsiders in the bay he thought he had an answer for everything.

Harvey, vainly trying to control his seething anger, explained what had happened in the gym. He described the eruption, the ensuing Pandemonium and the horrific stench that had permeated the gym. It was all Taco Heaven's fault, he stated flatly. They were liable. The public needed to be protected. Warnings should be put on all Big Horton labels. He wanted his money back.

Harvey was forced to file a lawsuit against Taco Heaven. He asked for $3.99, which was the sale price for the two Big Hortons. He also asked for two hundred million dollars in punitive damages (one hundred million for each of the two Big Hortons he had consumed) and $1.99 for a new pair of underwear. The lawsuit was eventually dropped after Taco Heaven sent an official letter of apology to Snooty Peterson and the principal. Harvey was further mollified when Taco Heaven presented him with ten Big Horton coupons.

A new Taco Heaven manager was hired and Harvey resumed his daily visits to the place. The Big Horton wrapper now depicts a nuclear explosion and a written gas warning that absolves the company from any liability. Harvey had yet to return to the high school gym, but this was because he still had another twelve months remaining on the ban the principal imposed.

Several months after the explosion Harvey was sitting on his screened in porch sipping a vodka and thinking about the event. He had always dabbled in hobbies that had to do with collecting and now his mind was working in this direction. He thought about the Elvis memorabilia that had at one time enthralled him. He fondly remembered his pet rock collection and his dirty sock drawer. Then there had been the time when he collected rubbage from the neighbor's trash cans. Lately, he had been impressed with Pizza Face Charlie's collection of Ripple Wine bottles. Pizza Face had a regular Ripple, a raspberry, a grape, a wintergreen, an extra strength and a cherry. There were only five other flavors of Ripple wine that had ever been produced and Pizza Face was out to collect a bottle of each. He figured that his collection would then be worth quite a lot of money. It was then that Harvey decided to start his own unique collection.

Harvey always had been bothered by gas. As a youngster his mother often referred to him as, "my cute, little fartie". Then, of course,

44

the incident at the school had made the front page of The Horton Bay Gazette, which led to an interview on the radio talk show, GOOD MORNING HORTON BAY. He decided that it was time to take advantage of this natural bodily function. Why not start a fart collection? Harvey mulled the idea over in his mind. He grew more excited by the minute. He had all the necessary equipment in the basement. There had to be hundreds of Mason jars on the shelves down there, left over from the days when his grandmother canned everything from the garden. There was rubber tubing from the old bicycle tires that were stacked in the corner. The tubing could be used to siphon off the finished product into the jars. And, his cupboards were stocked with plenty of chili, sauerkraut, red cabbage, navy beans, white beans, refried beans, pinto beans, sardines, pickles, anchovies, stewed tomatoes and Strohs beer.

Harvey had it all planned. He would only eat certain foods on certain days. Maybe sauerkraut for breakfast, lunch and dinner on Mondays. Tuesdays would be reserved for anchovies. Saturdays, of course, would be good beer days. Late at night he could use the rubber hose to tap into a really terrific fart. The gas would travel down the tube, into the jar, which would then be capped and labeled. His collection would grow daily. He would store the collection in a cool place away from the sunlight. Guests would be invited down to the cellar where they would marvel at the collection. For diversification he'd bottle some truly exotic gas. Perhaps he'd eat Chinese one day and name that particular bottle, WHO FLUNG POO, '72. He'd present it to his guests while having after dinner drinks following some special occasion dinner. He'd twist off the cap and let them all have a good whiff. Harvey had great dreams for this collection. He might even be able to sell some of his more popular gases. People might be willing to pay big money for a CHILI '75 or a PINTO BEAN '76. Harvey was beside himself with anticipation. This was going to be quite a project. Of course, he'd have to start a new corporation for this venture. No way was he going to split the profits with Madam Margo and Her All Seeing Glass Eye. After all, it would be his gas, not hers.

The collection never really became a reality. Oh, Harvey did start the collection, but the first night he uncapped an ANCHOVY '75 the candelabra on the dinner table exploded. A fire storm rushed through his house causing extensive damage. The next day Fire Chief LaBlance warned Harvey that this better be the end of the gas collection. Harvey readily agreed, but didn't bother to tell Chief LaBlance that a jar of RED CABBAGE '74 had been smuggled into a safe deposit box at the Horton Bay State Bank. There it would remain until New Year's Eve!

Chapter Four
THE FIRE BRIGADE

Years ago the Horton Bay Fire Brigade fell upon bad times by what has now been directly attributable to a rash of greasy skillet, cigarette ash tray and autumn leaf fires. The ever popular delicacy of Saber Tooth salmon filets produces a heavy, highly flammable grease when fried in a skillet. When the Saber Tooth salmon are running Horton Bay residents frequently fry the fish for breakfast, lunch and dinner. And just about as frequently a greasy skillet would burst into flames. Terrified villagers relied upon the Fire Brigade to respond in a timely manner. And back in the days when cigarette smoking was still popular it wasn't anything to see an ash tray filled to the brim with butts smoldering away. The good townspeople likewise relied upon the Fire Brigade to put these fires out. In the fall of the year there is no better smell than that of burning leaves, but when Mrs. Bagby's pile of leaves blew smoke into the open window of her next door neighbor, Beaulah Felts, it took the Fire Brigade over five hours to respond. By then Beaulah had doused the burning leaves with a bucket of lake water. A mob of thoroughly disgusted locals gathered at the General Store. The Constable was summoned to what he later described as a "very ugly scene." Violence was averted when it was announced that a new Fire Chief would be appointed.

Often times it's a case of being the right person, in the right place at the right time. Or maybe it's fate that thrusts an ordinary person into a heroic role. No matter. Brendon LaBlance was that person. Immediately upon being named the new Fire Chief, LaBlance was treated to a ticker tape parade through downtown Horton Bay. Fire Chief LaBlance then

46

addressed the cheering crowd from the front porch of the General Store. "You can count on me!" Chief LaBlance roared. "Wherever there's a skillet fire, I'll be there. Wherever an ash tray fire smolders, I'll be there. Wherever burning autumn leaves are licked by flames, I'll be there. My hoses, my water wagon, my Fire Brigade, we'll be all around."

The crowd was enthusiastic, but every town has its naysayers. In this case it was the Amazing Waldo. He wanted proof that the new Fire Brigade would be equipped to protect Horton Bay. After hours of negotiations it was decided that a "mock skillet fire" drill would be held at an undisclosed time and place in the bay. Once this challenge was thrown down, Fire Chief LaBlance started his troops on an extensive training program consisting of twice a day three hour workouts. Townspeople regularly showed up at the training sessions with placards bearing slogans of support. After several months of rigorous training Fire Chief LaBlance proclaimed that his troops were ready.

The City Council met to plan the mock fire. The actual time and place became one of the bay's most closely guarded secrets. Several of the Fire Chief's detractors have subsequently alleged that he had a paid informant on the inside who regularly passed sensitive information about the test to the Fire Brigade. Those allegations were extensively investigated by the Constable and his anti racketeering squad, but no wrong doing was ever discovered.

At last the surprise test took place. At precisely four o'clock in the afternoon, when it was widely known the Fire Chief would be sitting at Alexander's Bar a skillet chock full of Saber Tooth salmon fat was placed in the middle of the road in front of the General Store and the High Society Tree House. The grease was set on fire and a thirty foot high blaze danced above the skillet, forcing twelve cars, five motorcycles, eight bicycles and two dogs off the road. The fire alarm was sounded. The piercing wail from the fifty two sirens mounted atop two hundred foot tall towers shrieked for five hours until at last Fire Chief LaBlance and the Brigade arrived.

The horse drawn fire wagons thundered into town amidst a jubilant, noisy ovation from locals. The skillet fire was quickly doused and an enthusiastic crowd gave the Fire Brigade a ticker tape parade that culminated with the mayor proclaiming every Friday to be Fire Brigade Appreciation Day. Once again a group of detractors tried to convince the City Council that the Fire Chief and his troops had only responded to the alarm after the "happy hour" at Alexander's Bar was over.

The following winter the Fire Chief was forced to issue a priority

Level Four squirrel alert for the entire Horton Bay area. This alert covered both the downtown and suburban districts. According to Fire Chief LaBlance, the squirrel alert became necessary when locals began their annual acorn gathering in preparation for the cold winter months. This particular winter was predicted to be an especially harsh one so locals were gathering acorns in record numbers. A recently completed survey conducted by the Fire Brigade indicated that Horton Bay acorn bins were loaded to an all time high.

Since the early days when Three Fingers Holandaze had first settled in the area residents have burned acorns in their stoves for heat. Apparently, it was Three Fingers who discovered that acorns from the sturdy Horton Bay oaks burn hotter, longer and more efficiently than other hardwoods, fuel oil, propane gas and even Saber Tooth salmon oil. Birdy Johnson, the town's oldest resident announced, "I've already got my stove nice and hot. I've got enough acorns in my cellar to last the longest winter."

Fire Chief LaBlance responded in a Horton Bay Gazette interview by saying, "This type of greed is the exact reason why I have been forced to issue a Level Four Squirrel Alert. Trust me when I say that it would have been better to not gather as many acorns as you have than to have a bunch of hungry, mad squirrels wandering around out there!"

Horton Bay acorns are the main food source of the endangered White Spotted Tail Black Squirrel. The Fire Chief maintained that because Horton Bay residents had gathered acorns in record numbers there was the distinct possibility that the White Spotted Tail Black Squirrel would go hungry that winter. This particular type of squirrel turns exceptionally nasty when it is hungry. In The Horton Bay Gazette interview the Fire Chief pleaded with locals to quit gathering anymore acorns. The Fire Chief even went so far as to imply that it might be a wise move for residents to return some of their acorns to the woods. He indicated that if every household would take fifty bushels of acorns and scatter them about town a disaster could be averted. This idea was met with stiff resistance and even jeers around town. Birdy Johnson called in to the GOOD MORNING HORTON BAY radio show and declared, "if it's a matter of the White Spotted Tail Black Squirrel going hungry or me being cold then I say let the little bugger starve!"

Fire Chief LaBlance announced through his Press Secretary that the village should be prepared for a dramatic increase in squirrel attacks. The Level Four Alert cautions people not to walk underneath trees in Horton Bay, and under no conditions whatsoever should acorns be carried on your person.

The Friday following the issuance of the Squirrel Alert all Horton Bay schools were dismissed at noon when an angry group of White Spotted Tail Black Squirrels was seen massing on the west side of town. That night Fire Chief LaBlance had his squad raid the city supply of acorns, which had been gathered to heat the General Store. The acorns were delivered to the woods on the outskirts of town and left for the squirrels. The Fire Chief maintained that it was only this gesture that persuaded the angry mob of squirrels to disband. However, town locals were furious that the Fire Chief had capitulated so easily and demanded his resignation. In an attempt to counter this criticism the Fire Chief stated to a special meeting of the City Council that acorn burning has been proven to be a primary cause of chimney fires and that by returning the acorns to the woods he was in fact helping to protect the citizens of Horton Bay. The City Council voted to place Fire Chief LaBlance and his entire squad on Double Secret Probation, which as everyone knows is just one step short of Triple Secret Probation. Later that same winter the unthinkable occurred and they were put on Triple Secret Probation when the water in their fire hoses froze up during a routine skillet fire demonstration.

"How safe do you think I feel?" an irate Birdy Johnson asked the mayor.

"But, Birdy, this was only a test," the mayor had replied.

"Even if it was only a test there should have been antifreeze mixed in with that water. What if it had been my skillet that was on fire?" Birdy demanded.

Chief LaBlance countered with the defense that there was no antifreeze available since the City Council had cut this item from the budget. The Chief announced that if he and his squad would be taken off Triple Secret Probation then he would investigate forming a Flick Your Bic division of the Fire Brigade. This division would be responsible for holding cigarette lighters underneath the fire hose in order to warm the water. The Chief promised to test this new system at the next skillet fire drill.

The Horton Bay Fire Brigade did experience many moments of tremendous achievement. It was the Chief who trained a squadron of crows to act as tornado warning sirens. Whenever a funnel cloud was spotted the birds would fly to telephone wire perches around the village and sound the alarm. The Chief then issued instructions that all residents should take shelter in their outhouses. If the crows sounded a Level Three alert then the residents were told to dive into the holes in their outhouse. It may have been a messy solution, but the City Council credited Chief

49

LaBlance with saving many lives, and another ticker tape parade was held.

Fire Chief LaBlance was a big fan of double Dutch jump roping. His first year as Fire Chief he formed a Fire Brigade double Dutch jump roping team. Anytime the squad was not training they could be seen jump roping. They jumped all the time. The more they practiced the better they got. Then the Chief had the bright idea of entering his squad in various competitions around Northern Michigan. In their very first meet the Fire Brigade beat the middle school girls team from Boyne City. This was to be only the beginning of their success. The team quickly moved on to capture the All North Championship, then the All Michigan and finally the All Midwest.

The team was invited to participate in the Oslo Goodwill Jump, which was a prelude to NATO's Jump For Freedom competition. The Fire Brigade practiced for a minimum of eight hours a day in preparation for their first international jump. Then catastrophe struck. Lead jumper, Wee Willy Morrow, pulled a groin muscle and the team was forced to withdraw. The team physician advised the entire squad to take a month off from jumping and soak in the Horton Bay hot springs.

When the squad finally returned to competition it was with renewed vigor. They had spent the month soaking in the warm waters of the Horton Bay hot springs and studying films of the crack Russian squad. After a rigorous six months of training the Fire Chief announced that his squad was ready to resume competition and would be traveling to Amsterdam for the Dutch Double Dutch Derby. Then catastrophe struck again. Following a practice session in New York an assailant (later identified as the father of a Dutch double Dutch jumper) attacked Horton Bay's Battlin' Joe's left knee with a baseball bat. The assailant later confessed that he had been trying to knock the Horton Bay team out of the competition. The baseball bat attack was high, somehow missing Battlin' Joe's left knee, and it was subsequently announced that Battlin' Joe had left the team to sing soprano in the Horton Bay boy's choir.

Though the team never got to compete in the Dutch Double Dutch Derby they did manage to regain the love and admiration of Horton Bay. Still sensitive to criticism, the Fire Chief acknowledged that his squad would not jump in any more meets, but would confine their jumping to a hobby only performed around the fire house. "We want to spend more time in Horton Bay," he stated. "This is where we're needed."

A year later, however, his troops left Horton Bay for San Francisco to participate in the World Bubble Gum Bubble Blowing Championship. Apparently, the Brigade discovered while they were sitting around the fire house chewing bubble gum that they could blow amazingly large bubbles, especially when they chewed the grape flavor. The Horton Bay squad took first place in size bubble, third in shape bubble (shaped like a miniature Hortness monster) and fourth in artistic expression. Following that competition Squirty Jones resigned from the Fire Brigade to join the Professional Bubble Blowers (PBB) Tour.

The Fire Brigade still remains an essential part to the overall safety of Horton Bay. They were credited several years ago with saving the village from sure destruction. A huge bird had been terrorizing the bay. The bird, believed to be a descendant of the Paleozoic creature that roamed the upper Midwest some two million years ago, kept Horton Bay residents prisoners in their own homes as it soared two miles above the bay in search of prey. Fire Chief Lablance advised residents to travel in the safety of numbers until his Search and Rescue Squad (aided by the elite Horton Bay Swat Team) was able to dispose of the bird.

The prehistoric bird is believed to have subsisted off large mammals. Using a special telephoto lens Fire Chief LaBlance was able to take fifteen roles of pictures of the bird. The Fire Chief estimated that the creature had a wing span of approximately eighty feet. The Horton Bay Bird Watchers Society theorizes that a massive prehistoric egg probably had been buried eons ago during one of the Horton Bay volcano eruptions. More than likely a shifting of the Hortonian Fault caused the egg to roll into the Horton Creek hot springs where it hatched. The bird had a piercing scream that could be heard for several miles. That scream was the only warning that the bird was diving at super sonic speeds and hunting for a resident, who had somehow wandered away from their group. The bird was credited with breaking the sound barrier a record fifteen days in a row. Since this was a violation of the Horton Bay noise ordinance the Constable was called in on the case.

Maggie Frump, a fudgie who weighs about four hundred pounds, was plucked from the bay as she sunbathed on the family barge. The huge bird apparently carried Ms. Frump to an altitude of three thousand feet. The fudgie managed to escape when she squirted the bird in the face with pepper mace, which Ms. Frump later stated she carried in order to keep pick up artists from bothering her when she visited the Eager Beaver Tavern on Saturday nights.

The bird was finally shot down when Chief LaBlance set up the Brigade's new high velocity water jet along the high altitude corridor the bird had been most frequently using. When the bird was finally sighted the Brigade fired a volley of warning water streams across the bird's flight

51

path. When the bird ignored the shots it was brought down by a blast of super charged water. The bird crashed into the bay and the Search and Rescue Squad was able to capture it using a huge Blue Gill net. The bird can now be seen as part of Horton Bay Tours, Ltd. octopus show where every afternoon it acts out a fight to the death with Igor, the large male octopus that Harvey bought from a fishing trawler in Key West, Florida.

The Horton Bay Road Warriors honored Chief LaBlance for his efforts by making him a Member for Life. The Road Warriors had for some time been trying to improve relations with the village and saw making Chief LaBlance a member as a step in the right direction. Years ago a riot occurred in downtown Horton Bay when the Constable ordered the Road Warriors to take their flag down from the General Store. The riot consisted of the Road Warriors threatening to ride their motorcycles through the bay in excess of the thirty five mile an hour speed limit. Later, the Road Warriors offered to make amends with the village by hosting a benefit beer and shot chugging contest at the now defunct Kit Kat Club. The benefit would be to help raise funds for the new Horton Bay subway system, which had just received approval from the City Council. This plan called for inmates of the Horton Bay Correctional Facility to excavate the old tunnel that Pete and Re-Pete Hokum had dug years earlier when they escaped from jail. The original tunnel measured three miles in length and plans called for the inmates to dig another six miles. This tunnel would then be shorn up, tracks would be laid and people would be able to travel from one end of the village to the other in less than half an hour. The original plan had been disputed by the downtown Merchants Association, but they dropped their complaint when it was learned that there would be a subway stop at the General Store, the Eager Beaver Tavern and the Tree House. The subway system was estimated to cost two hundred dollars. An advertising campaign directed at fudgies urged them to make a donation at any one of the five coffee tins that The Constable had nailed to trees around the bay.

The Road Warrior benefit was a big success. Fire Chief LaBlance won the beer chugging contest and The Salamander won the shot contest. The Constable arrested both men later that night when they stole a basket of hard boiled eggs from Misty Sorenson's kitchen window. Misty was to have used the eggs to make her famous egg salad for the Road Warriors annual Drink and Dial Party. This party is held every year at the Eager Beaver Tavern and consists of several hours of drinking. This is followed by using the pay phone and seeing how many overseas collect telephone calls will be accepted by perfect strangers in an hour's time. The record stands at one hundred and two.

The Fire Chief and The Salamander received a special citation from the City Council for digging a record quarter of a mile of the subway tunnel during their one night in jail. That record also still stands.

Chapter Five
THE HOSPITAL

Hortonians are a very independent lot. They like to think that the bay is one hundred percent self sufficient. All they need is themselves, and then there is no mountain that can't be climbed.

That's why it particularly galled locals that whenever there was an illness, a baby to be born, tonsils that needed yanking or an appendix that went bad they were forced, forced mind you, to go to Petoskey. Now there is absolutely nothing wrong with the Petoskey hospital or the doctors there, it's just all part of that civic pride thing that makes Hortonians so self reliant. They wanted their own hospital. But Horton Bay had no hospital. The good people's hands were tied, and had been for years.

It seems that the City Council, pushed and goaded by Horton Bay Tours, Ltd., was hell bent on growth, the type of growth that brought fudgies and cone suckers (customers with money in their hands) to Horton Bay. Harvey Whippleman constantly sought budget allocations for projects like the 90,000 seat domed stadium. He pointed to NFL expansion cities like Jacksonville and Charlotte as examples of what could happen in the bay. Build a stadium and they will come, was what he said. And indeed, once the domed stadium was approved a fellow by the name of Louie (The Lip) Rigatoni arrived in town with promises of bringing an NFL team to Horton Bay. Louie The Lip informed the City Council that his investment group was prepared to win a franchise for the bay. The Lip's plan called for 3,125 luxury condominium sky boxes to be built in the proposed stadium. Each box would sell for $15,000.00. When every box had been sold The Lip and his investment group would be in a position to woo the NFL. As The Lip stated, "The nearly forty seven million will take me, I mean, us a long way!" It was pointed out that in order for the stadium to accommodate that many sky boxes each box could only be big enough to seat two people and one would have to sit directly behind the other. The City Council voted to move forward with the stadium and The Lip's proposal. Plans for a Horton Bay General Hospital were once again put on hold. It was later discovered that The Lip was wanted by the state of Florida regarding a real estate deal involving the Everglades.

Then, of course, there were the plans for the Taz Mahorton, the world's largest trailer motel. Horton Bay Tours, Ltd. had complained that there were not enough motel rooms in Horton Bay to accommodate the large number of visitors it brought to the bay every year. The tour company sought city funds for the construction of a one hundred story high trailer motel. As Harvey so eloquently said at the special City Council meeting, which was called to vote on the plan, "This proposal; would actually result in two benefits for Horton Bay. Our community has for a long time suffered the problem of what to do with our old trailers and mobile homes. Our forests and swamps are no longer pristine. Now, when taking a leisurely walk in the woods the vista is interrupted by abandoned trailers, rusting and rotting away. It's a blight on our community, something you'd expect to see in East Jordan! Add to that the problem of not having enough rooms for our cherished fudgie and cone sucker. I, Harvey Whippleman, mayor of this fine village," (his address was interrupted at this point by a heckler who screamed, "and President of Horton Bay Tours, Ltd.!'), "firmly believe that we can take these discarded trailers and build a wonderful motel. I've counted over one hundred trailers and mobile homes in the woods. If we stacked one on top of the other we would have a wonderful one hundred story motel." An enthusiastic City Council agreed and plans for a hospital were once again put on hold.

Hotonians are a hardy lot. They simply refuse to take no for an answer. If the good people wanted their own hospital then they would find a way to get one, with or without the City Council's funding. A group of concerned citizens got together one night at Myrtle's Consignment Shop to discuss the situation. Skimpy Sucker pointed out that since he'd sold off his cows he had no further need for his old dairy barn. The barn consisted of some twenty thousand square feet, which would be large enough for a hospital. Skimpy gallantly offered to donate the dairy barn to the city if the City Council would agree in return to give him a large tax deduction. It seems that Skimpy's great grandfather had been a country doctor in East Jordan back in the days when Three Fingers Holandaze was settling

55

Horton Bay. Skimpy's great grandfather, I. M., had set up shop in East Jordan, but was forced to flee to Horton Bay when he was caught double billing Blue Cross Blue Shield. I.M. went on to become a revered physician in Horton Bay and now Skimpy wanted to honor his great grandfather by having his dairy barn named the Horton Bay Sucker Hospital. Never wanting to ignore a good deal the City Council readily accepted the offer, but on the condition that the furnishing and maintenance of the hospital be privately funded.

In order to raise funds for the hospital Fire Chief LaBlance formed a special Road Kill Patrol. The patrol requisitioned Battlin' Joe's '54 Chevy as the official Road Kill Emergency Vehicle. Red cellophane was taped over the headlights and Wild Bill and Battlin' Joe were issued Road Kill Patrol badges. Their job was to roam the village streets in search of road kill, an item long considered a culinary delicacy in the bay. The badges gave the Patrol the right to confiscate any road kill that had already been pried up from the street. The Patrol would gather all the available road kill and then the meat would be used for the Sunday afternoon bake sale and barbecue held every week in the Three Fingers Memorial Park. All proceeds from the road kill barbecue went to benefit the hospital. It wasn't long before there was enough money in the hospital fund to finance a shopping spree at the local Goodwill. The first year two old sofas, an end table and six lamps (two needed repair) were purchased. Two beds were discovered alongside the road with a sign that read "Free for the taking" and Horton Bay Fisheries donated an old fish cleaning table that quickly became the primary operating table for the new hospital. The front reception desk was the old pool table from the Eager Beaver Tavern and the nurse's station was a folding card table that bounced off the back end of a fudgies camper two summers earlier and had been stored in the General Store's garage where it had been gathering dust. A group of civic minded citizens spent their free time finishing off the dairy barn's interior. Unfortunately, no one had had any previous experience with the inside of a hospital so all the doors were cut too narrow for beds to pass through. After the fact, the local carpenters remedied this problem by cutting the bottom half of every door away so that the bottom was a foot wider on each side than was the top. As long as no beds over a three foot height were picked up from the roadside then there would be no problem getting them through the doors.

Since there were no doctors in Horton Bay a Search Committee was formed to find one for the hospital. After six months of meetings the Search Committee decided to hire a professional recruiter out of Detroit.

This "headhunter" promised the Search Committee that in return for his fifty thousand dollar fee a qualified doctor would be found in a matter of days. The Road Kill Patrol was sent back to duty and more barbecues were held. Once the fifty grand had been raised and deposited in the headhunter's account the village sat back and waited. In less than twenty four hours the new doctor arrived in town. That night a welcoming reception was held at the Whippleman Hall. The doctor, a certain Sid (The Kid) Malarkey was from Miami, Florida. Most recently he had been selling used cars at a place called Fast Freddie's. His credentials indicated that he had been the top salesman for five out of the last six months, which greatly impressed the Search Committee. Prior to working at Fast Freddie's, The Kid had operated his own lot, a place called Sid's House of Values. That lot closed following an investigation by the state's Attorney General's office. The Kid's resume listed a medical degree from Rolanda University in Bogata, Columbia.

Before long the hospital was taking care of all of Horton Bay's medical needs. There was the nursery, the operating room, the emergency room, the geriatric center, the intensive care unit. All operated efficiently. It was a place that marked the beginning and end of many lives. The hospital became a symbol of Horton Bay's independence, a place of great joy and of great sadness.

It became a rite of passage for young boys to sneak around the hospital grounds peeking in windows. Often they were able to catch a glimpse of The Kid giving a physical to one of the local women. If the boys were lucky they got to see an exposed breast or perhaps half of a buttock. It was all great fun. Part of the fun was outwitting the hospital security guard, who roamed the grounds in a beat up Volkswagon bus. The boys hid in the bushes, crouched beneath the hospital windows. Playing pranks on the geriatric wing provided some of the best laughs. The boys discovered that for the old folks, passing gas was as contagious as yawning. If one did it, they all did it. The boys would sneak up to one of the open windows of the wing and one of them would make a loud farting sound by holding the palms of his hands to his mouth. Another boy would then let out a long, satisfied groan. Pretty soon, all the old geezers would be passing gas. There'd be high squeaks, muffled roars, long, drawn out whistles. It sounded much like the Horton Bay Symphony Orchestra warming up before a performance. Then an exasperated nurse would rush in and turn on the ceiling fans.

The boys also witnessed a lot more. They learned what it meant to die. One evening they wandered upon the open window of a man who hadn't long to live. The boys peeked into the window and saw the old man lying in bed. He was surrounded by his caring family, a wife of forty two years, a grown son and daughter, a sister. The family stood around the man's bed, every person touching him. His wife tenderly held his hand, the daughter stroked his forehead, the son patted his shoulder, the sister rubbed his arm. The man was surrounded by love and security. He had only another ninety seconds to live. His breathing was very shallow and irregular, but his eyes were clear. He turned his head and looked out the window. He saw the trees and the evening wind blowing through the high branches. Beyond, he could see the deep blue water of Horton Bay. He'd led a good life and been very happy, yet at this moment he now thought about the girl he'd been in love with back when he'd been a senior at Horton Bay High. She was so very beautiful and he remembered that she had loved him back and that they had talked of getting married in four years after they graduated from Horton Bay University. They were so young and happy. They wanted to have children, three children, and even picked names out for each child. Now, he wondered what had ever become of her and whether or not she ever thought about him. He closed his eyes and remembered those long ago, innocent days. At last he stretched out his hand and feebly waved it into the empty space in front of his face. "What is it, Dad?" his son asked. All the man could see was his young girlfriend's smiling face, and very carefully he brushed the golden hair from her eyes.

Two windows down the boys could hear a young woman with cancer saying her prayers. The pinkish glow from the fading sunset barely lit the room. Earlier that day she had been told that her situation was not good. She was asked if there was anybody she would like to be called. She had no family, only her religion, and now she clung to that and she was comforted. The boys listened as she whispered into the still night air:

Hail, Mary, full of grace the Lord is with thee.
Blessed art thou amongst women
And blessed is the fruit of thy womb, Jesus
Holy Mary, mother of God pray for us sinners
Now, and at the hour of our death
Amen

There is death, even in Horton Bay. And life goes on, the cycle continues.

Horton Bay also had no place to take a sick pet so Sid The Kid Malarkey opened a veterinary clinic on the other side of the building, thereby killing two birds with one stone, so to speak. The boys now crept around the building to pay a visit to Tiny Monroe's parakeet that accidentally had fallen into a kettle of Big Joey B's home brew. Both the bird and Big Joey B had been brought to the clinic to sober up. Both were doing fine.

Chapter Six
CRIME IN THE BAY

The extremely low crime rate in Horton Bay was one of the reasons so many people wanted to immigrate there. Had there been crime there probably never would have been a reason for a Border Patrol or falsified documents that made a person a local. People felt safe in the bay. After all, besides an occasional barking dog or littered pop can, the Constable had a pretty cushy job.

When Three Fingers Holandaze first paddled into the bay he spotted thousands of pink flamingos. The magnificent birds were everywhere, strutting on the wide beaches, floating on the water. Their brilliant color had a powerful affect on Three Fingers and he immediately made the pink flamingo the national bird of Horton Bay. Three Fingers is known to have fashioned the first pink flamingo yard decoration in honor of the bird. He forced Stinky and Butter Milk to do the same. Eventually, the habit spread to the Indians. They placed pink flamingo yard decorations in front of their teepees. As the years went by it became a tradition to place one , two or even more of the beloved mascot in front of your house or wigwam. Years later, visitors to the bay liked the lawn decorations so well that they purchased pink flamingo kits from the Whippleman Pink Flamingo Company, took them back to their home towns and proudly displayed the bird in their own yards. Today it is nearly impossible to travel anywhere in the country and not see a plastic, pink flamingo in someone's yard, which is yet another wonderful way people honor Horton Bay.

People in Horton Bay love their pink, plastic flamingos. They're like family. The birds are always given names, and quite frequently they are passed down from one generation to the next. It's not uncommon for a son to grow up, marry and receive a pink, plastic flamingo for a wedding present. Perhaps he'll give his bride another one to celebrate their first wedding anniversary. Then with the passing of his parents the son would inherit their flamingos. If the son has siblings then maybe his parent's flock might be split up with one bird going to a brother, another to a sister. Most of the time families liked to keep the birds together, the thought being that it might be somewhat traumatic to split the birds up. After all, the flamingos might have been standing together, mired side by side in the same lawn for years.

Crime is always deplorable, but a crime in Horton Bay involving the disappearance of somebody's pink, plastic flamingos is particularly heinous. One peaceful, quiet Friday night the Vander Whipples (Horace Whippleman, a nephew of Harvey's had changed his name to Vander Whipple fifteen years earlier because he thought it sounder classier), one of Horton Bay's most prominent families spent the evening on their front lawn talking to Homer and Ethel, their two pink, plastic flamingos. Hardly a summer night went by that the Vander Whipples didn't sit in their aluminum lawn chairs, sip ten or twelve Long Island ice teas and have a nice chat with their birds. All summer Homer and Ethel stood stuck in the front lawn next to the miniature plastic wishing well and white painted tractor tire that was planted with dandelions, the official flower of Horton Bay. From their vantage point Homer and Ethel could watch the traffic as it passed on the Boyne City Road. Homer had been with the Vander Whipples for four years. He married Ethel two years later when Ethel was purchased at Horton Bay Hardware and Sundries. It was a beautiful garden wedding. Ninety six pink plastic flamingos belonging to other Horton Bay families were in attendance. The Horton Bay Gazette devoted an entire front page to the affair.

When the Vander Whipples retired for the evening Homer and Ethel seemed to be in good spirits. It was just another Friday evening in the bay. It was about eight o'clock Saturday morning when Mrs. Vander Whipple happened to glance out her kitchen window. Her eyes grew big with alarm. She immediately felt as though she'd been kicked in the stomach. She couldn't breathe. Her heart raced and she swooned. Homer and Ethel were gone!

Mrs. Vander Whipple fought to scream, but there was no sound. At last she managed a feeble cry for help and Horace came running from the bedroom, still in his pajamas. He stared in disbelief at the empty spot beside the miniature wishing well. Together the Vander Whipples rushed to the front lawn crying for Homer and Ethel. They listened, but the only sounds were the morning birds chirping in the trees. Horace bent down and studied the ground.

"Look, there's been a heroic struggle here," he said, pointing to some scuff marks in the grass.

"Homer! Ethel! Where are you?" Mrs. Vander Whipple wailed.

Her screams brought out the neighbors and before long there was a crowd. The men studied the ground looking for clues. The women comforted Mrs. Vander Whipple. Finally, someone thought to call 911. About an hour later the Constable arrived on the scene along with Horton

Bay forensics. The "crime scene" as the Constable called the front lawn was cordoned off. The wishing well was dusted for prints. The Constable concurred, there had definitely been a struggle, a monumental one at that, for he had discovered pink paint streaked along one side of the wishing well. A glove with pink paint on it was also discovered. The Constable and his deputies interviewed all the neighbors. No one saw or heard anything that was the least bit unusual or suspicious. The Constable wrote up his report, promised the Vander Whipples that he would create a special task force to investigate the crime and that justice would be served. That afternoon he assigned the case to his top two detectives, identical twins, Ron and Ronrico Bobsey. The Constable had liked these two from the start because they were so identical that it was nearly impossible to tell them apart. The Constable felt this was a tremendous boon to the force because it would confuse the criminal element.

Once word of the crime had spread through the bay the public was outraged. Small groups gathered to discuss the matter. Worried knots of men clustered on the front porch of the General Store to discuss how best to protect their homes and families. Panic spread. Families took their pink, plastic flamingos into the safety of their homes. The Vander Whipples waited. And they waited. That first night they were unable to sleep. They sat up all night peering out their front window into the inky darkness, wondering where, oh where, were Homer and Ethel. Periodically, Mrs. Vander Whipple would go to the door and call for her birds. She called and called until finally one of the neighbors yelled, "Shut up, ya old bitch!" Then it was quiet in the bay, but through that first long night no one felt safe.

The next day The Horton Bay Gazette printed a notice in the Personal Section of the paper. The notice appeared just under a note of congratulations from someone named Jeff that read:

TO JUDY: I'm not too proud to admit it when I've made a terrible mistake. I was so wrong when I called you a fat pig and said that I hoped you'd get hit by a car. I now realize that I need you more than ever before. Please give me another chance, Judy. I love you and miss you tons (no pun intended). Without you the life has seeped from my soul. I am nothing without you. Please accept my phone calls. I really want us to get back together. Love, Jeff. P.S. Congratulations on winning the Michigan State Lottery!

Directly underneath this note appeared the ransom note:

TO THE PEOPLE MISSING THE PINK, PLASTIC FLAMINGOS: If you ever want to see your pets again then take $5.00 in small unmarked bills and leave them in an old, brown paper bag underneath the Horton Bay High Society tree house. Do not make any attempt to notify the Constable. So far the birds have been unharmed, but patience and time is running out. M.H.

The Vander Whipples panicked and notified the Constable, but he'd already read the paper. Ron and Ronrico Bobsey were following up on the lead. After eating the lunch their mother had packed they took the empty brown paper lunch bag and stuffed it with the discarded sandwich bags. They placed the bag beneath the tree house and then disguised themselves as trash cans. They conducted their "stake out" for six days. At about twilight on the sixth day a furtive figure approached the brown paper bag. The twins braced themselves. They watched as the person glided in and out of the shadows. When the person finally picked up the bag the twins sprang into action. It took about forty five minutes to subdue the suspect, who turned out to be the Constable. He was following up on a littering complaint that had been filed by The Salamander. It seems that The Salamander had already looked inside the bag thinking that he might find a bottle of wine with a remaining swallow or two. The twins had somehow missed spotting The Salamander. Later, the twins confessed to napping and the Constable officially reprimanded them for sleeping on the job. Regardless, the real criminal never showed up to collect the paper bag.

Two days later a picture of Homer and Ethel appeared in The Horton Bay Gazette. The picture showed the two obviously distraught flamingos with nooses around their long necks. The previous day's copy of the newspaper was lying on the ground before them indicting that as of that day the birds were still okay. Beneath the picture was a note warning the Vander Whipples to pay up within twenty four hours or else. The Constable called the Vander Whipples and told them to prepare for the worst. The Constable then located Fire Chief LaBlance at the Eager Beaver Tavern and ordered him to issue a Flamingo Alert. The Fire Chief immediately imposed a curfew, which required that all pink, plastic flamingos be off the street by sunset. Any flamingos who did not obey the curfew would be fined fifty cents.

The case got a big break when a finger print lifted from the miniature wishing well was matched against some prints in the Constable's file. The prints were from a certain Mary Harris, who had the distinction of being Horton Bay's oldest resident, and she was the only person in the

63

bay who had the initials M.H., which had been the signature on the first ransom note. The twins slowly were putting together a case.

Mary was considered by her neighbors to be a quiet person, who enjoyed playing hop scotch and arm wrestling at the Eager Beaver. The twins, still disguised as trash cans, searched the outside of Mary's house. In the backyard, next to her own trash can, they discovered a glove that matched the one found at the crime scene. At that moment Mary walked out her back door with some garbage that consisted of coffee grounds, empty vodka bottles and a month old issue of Horton Bay Publication's *Porno in the Bay*. She mistook one of the twins for her own trash can and dumped her garbage on top of him. The twins doffed their disguises and after a Kung Fu fight that lasted several minutes were able to handcuff the suspect.

The Constable refused to release any information to the press following the arrest for fear that a vigilante group of angry citizens would form a lynch mob. He kept the issue of *Porno in the Bay* as evidence. He also allowed the suspect to be photographed, but made her wear the black cat burglar's mask that was found hidden beneath the floor boards of her living room by Bingo, the Snake Hunting Dog, who had been rented out for the investigation. Ron and Ronrico proudly posed on either side of Mary for the photograph. The picture never was printed in the paper because the paper's editor thought that his photographer had mistakenly taken a double exposure. This tickled the Constable and he privately bragged that this was proof that his theory of hiring twins as deputies in order to confuse the criminal element was working.

It later was determined that Mary Harris, alias Cheese Cake Mama, was wanted in fifteen states for kidnapping pink, plastic flamingos. In her confession she stated, "I was attracted to Horton Bay simply because of the sheer number of flamingos in the community." Cheese Cake Mama was sentenced to five days at Horton Bay's maximum security prison, Hortontraz, but received three days off for time served while she was awaiting trial. She spent the remaining two days working on the subway tunnel. Following her release she went on to even greater fame when she set a Horton Bay record of saying the alphabet 12,476 times without making a mistake.

The crime rate in Horton Bay took a drop following the arrest of Mary Harris, but it wasn't long before the Constable had another problem. Horton Bay Bank and Trust had a long standing habit of providing a bowl of mints at the teller's window. Customers were encouraged to take one, especially if the teller thought they had bad breath. A survey, which had been conducted by a private firm hired by the bank, determined that some people were taking more than one mint with each visit to the bank. In fact, the consulting firm concluded that the number of mints taken from the bowl had increased a whopping seven percent over the last year! The Constable was alerted and he wasted no time in declaring, "Obviously, a local business like Horton Bay Bank and Trust cannot and will not tolerate such abuse. My office has been asked to help with what we consider to be theft. It may be white collar crime, but no matter what color it is, it's still crime."

Later that same day the Constable was lounging around the General Store when he heard that Bingo, the Snake Hunting Dog had been laid off by Horton Bay Tours, Ltd. Apparently, Bingo went on what the tour company had called an unauthorized strike following a new pooper scooper ordinance that the company put into effect the previous month. A company spokesperson commented that, "For a long time now we've felt that Bingo's attitude was not the greatest. He howled at the moon, chased passing cars and relieved himself on one of our neighbor's trash cans, who later turned out to be Deputy Ronrico Bobsey. When he refused to comply with the pooper scooper ordinance we had no other alternative but to let him go. Besides, the snake hunting attraction has been off the last couple of years. Nobody's interested in hunting snakes anymore. They're all out looking for empty pop bottles." There was no immediate comment from Bingo, though The Horton Bay Gazette learned that he was plenty pissed over his dismissal.

The Constable informed The Horton Bay Gazette that he intended to form a new canine unit called, Apprehend, Search and Safety, which eventually would consist of nine dogs (any more than nine dogs in Horton Bay required a kennel license). The Constable's new ASS 9 Patrol would be a strong deterrent to crime in the bay. It was decided to put Bingo through a rigorous training program conducted by Fire Chief LaBlance. The Fire Chief stated, "We're training Bingo to watch that bowl of mints. By the time he graduates from our twelve week program he'll be one of the best in the business."

Bingo disappeared after only three weeks into the training program. He took the bowl of mints and was reportedly last seen selling Petoskey stones in East Jordan. The Constable immediately issued an All Points Bulletin on Bingo and his paw prints were entered into the computer. Horton Bay Bank and Trust used to hand out dog biscuits to their drive thru customers who had a pet in the car. That long time and popular practice was halted the day following Bingo's getaway. Initially, the bank's customers were upset that there would be no more dog biscuits handed out. "It was merely a matter of principle," Shifty Con, the bank's President, reported at their next stockholder's meeting. People in Horton Bay were finally convinced. After all, Shifty was a well respected bank president so the people gave him their support.

The only dissenter was Miss Purebottom, the Headmistress at the Purebottom School for Girls. Miss Purebottom didn't like Shifty Con. She thought he was a disgrace to the community ever since the night she saw him as he arrived back at his house after a night of frolicking at the Eager Beaver Tavern. Earlier, he had stopped at the General Store and bought a brisket of corned beef and two heads of cabbage. Had he not gotten side tracked by a game of butt darts (participants wedge a quarter into the crack of their butt, squat over a coffee cup and try to release the coin so that it falls into the cup) at the Eager Beaver Tavern he would have cooked his favorite Saint Patty's day dinner. After the butt darts he and the Fire Chief started drinking Pile Drivers, which is their favorite cocktail. A Pile Driver consists of two parts vodka and one part prune juice. The men drank fifteen Pile Drivers each before switching to Depth Charges, another drink they liked a lot. A Depth Charge has been a popular drink in Horton Bay since the Three Fingers Holandaze days. It consists of a mug of beer and a shot of whiskey. The bartender serves each separately. The customer then holds the shot glass of whiskey over the mug of beer and yells very loudly, "Bombs away!" He then drops the entire shot glass into the mug. Next he chugs the beer until the shot glass is also empty and slides down the mug and caught by the person's mouth. After twelve Depth Charges and an Irish coffee Shifty decided to head for home.

Shifty's driveway runs up to his house at about a thirty degree angle. When he got out of his car it was a real struggle. The world was spinning around and he was now seeing three of everything. He'd parked haphazardly and the car was on an angle so that the door was facing downhill. He reached inside, vainly trying to grab his bag of corn beef and cabbage. Once he had the bag slung over his shoulder the bag tore and both heads of cabbage dropped to the ground and then slowly rolled about ten yards down the driveway. Shifty followed in pursuit. When he reached the cabbage he bent to pick one up, but just then his foot kicked the other head and it rolled another ten yards down the driveway. Then he kicked the first and it rolled further along. This pattern continued, Shifty reeling and stumbling after the cabbage, until both heads came to a rest on the flat part of the drive that was near the street. By now Shifty was exasperated and angry. He steadied himself, tried to focus on the cabbage and planned his attack. He had rapidly run out of energy. He realized that he probably had only one more chance left in him to get his cabbage back. If he didn't get the cabbage this last time he'd have to leave it for the raccoons. He forced his eyes to zero in on the two round objects. He took one last deep breath. Then he hurled himself into the air. He sailed, with his arms outstretched, like a giant bird in flight. With a tremendous thud he landed. For a moment he was shaken, but finally he realized that he was on top of both heads of cabbage. He grabbed them and cradled them happily in his arms. He had the cabbage! He was ecstatic. He began laughing like a wild man. He was overcome with joy. He kissed and salaciously fondled the cabbage, delighted as he was.

Just then Miss Purebottom, who was out looking for Miss Fluff Fluff, her cat, pulled her car into Shifty's driveway so that she could turn around. The beam of her car's headlights framed Shifty just as a stage spotlight encircles an actor. There he was, lying on the ground, hugging and kissing his two heads of cabbage. He was so drunk he never even saw the car lights. He merely continued to laugh hysterically and fondle the cabbage. Miss Purebottom was horrified. The next day she closed her account at Horton Bay Bank and Trust and moved her business to the Whippleman Savings and Loan, which had recently opened. Then several months later when she heard that Shifty's bank was eliminating dog biscuits for their customer's pets she suspected that there was some underlying, kinky reason for the decision. One thing was for sure. She immediately informed the dietician at the Purebottom School for Girls that cabbage was never again to be put on the menu.

Some people say that they've spotted Miss Purebottom driving by Shifty's house late at night. They say that she'll slow the car and scan the driveway with a longing look on her face. If these stories are true then it's thought that Miss Purebottom must surely have been in bed when, helplessly, her mind would return to the night when she'd seen Shifty rolling about on the ground. She'd remember his hands, those large, strong hands, caressing, tugging, toying with the two round, shiny heads of cabbage. And his lips had been kissing the cabbage, his tongue searching and probing. Those must have been the times that she got out of bed and drove by Shifty's house hoping for another show, or perhaps a bit more.

The Horton Bay Sanitation Department has an ordnance that they are the only authority allowed to pick up garbage in the village. They have a monopoly and as a result get away with charging inordinately high fees. In fact, it's downright ridiculous how much is charged for trash pick up. Customers are forced to purchase the department's special trash bags. On

67

pick up days the roadsides are cluttered with the department's trash bags. No Horton Bay Sanitation Department trash bag, no trash picked up. That's just the way things are in the bay. But there are always a few residents who are out to beat the system. They refuse to buy the official trash bags. They pack small amounts of their trash in plastic grocery sacks and sneak these into the public waste cans at Horton Bay Gas and Save or the General Store. It may take twenty or so such trips, but eventually the trash is gone and it didn't cost a cent.

One day, however, the Area Manager of the Gas and Save (he is responsible for all forty two Gas and Save stores in Horton Bay) was just pulling up to pump number twenty eight when he spotted Martha Gelhaven, Horton Bay's wealthiest resident, lugging a huge bag of garbage to the Gas and Save dumpster. The Sanitation Department charges Gas and Save a few hundred dollars a month for just this one dumpster, so the Area Manager was furious. By the time he had run back to the dumpster Mrs. Gelhaven had already driven away. The Area Manager removed the big bag of garbage from the dumpster, took it inside the store and called the Constable. By the time the Constable showed up three days later the bag of Mrs. Gelhaven's garbage was getting fairly ripe. Fire Chief LaBlance was summoned and after determining that there was nothing explosive in the bag he threatened to shut down the store unless the garbage was removed. He said it posed a health problem to the general public. The Constable seized the garbage as evidence and took it to his house where he spread the contents out on his living room floor. He thought there might be some sort of clue hidden in the rotting slime that would identify the owner. Meanwhile, Mrs. Gelhaven somehow found out that her trash had been plucked from the Gas and Save dumpster. She was outraged and called the Constable's office, demanding that her garbage be returned at once. How dare the Constable go through her trash! The nerve!

At first, the Constable agreed that Mrs. Gelhaven deserved to get her trash back. After all, she was Horton Bay's wealthiest resident and should receive some sort of preferential treatment. Besides, she had been a very large contributor to the Constable's last campaign. He assured Mrs. Gelhaven that as soon as he got up from his afternoon nap he'd pack her garbage up and return it to her. When the Constable awoke from his three hour nap he sat up in bed and sleepily began to wonder just why Mrs. Gelhaven had been so adamant that her trash be returned. And then it hit him! She must be hiding something!

Maybe the old bag wasn't as wealthy as she made everyone believe.

Now that the Constable thought about it, he realized how much everyone in the village resented all her talk about money. Perhaps there was a disconnect notice in her trash from Horton Bay Power and Light. No, the Constable thought, she must be hiding something bigger. He got up and surveyed the trash strewn about his living room floor. And there it was tucked between the remnants of what had once been a canteloupe. He saw the neck of a liquor bottle. She must be a closet drinker! Wait a minute, he thought. She's always throwing those fancy cocktail parties so what's so strange about an empty liquor bottle? He plucked the bottle off the floor anyway. It was the cheapest brand of vodka sold. The Constable closed his eyes and tried to remember what brand of vodka he'd seen on her bar the night she summoned him to quiet some noisy crickets in her back yard. Yeah, now he remembered. Her bar had displayed the most expensive vodka made in the world. Maybe she was siphoning the cheap brand into an empty bottle of the expensive stuff! That's a trick the cheap phonies in Charlevoix were always pulling. Then his eyes fell upon a subscription renewal form for *Porno in the Bay*! Now he feverishly searched through the trash. He suspected there might even be a nude photo or two of Mrs. Gelhaven. It was even possible that the old bag was having an affair. After all, now he recalled seeing Peter Bark Like a Dog, an old Indian, who lived in the village, raking leaves at Mrs. Gelhaven's place. Maybe Bark Like a Dog had written a tender love note. The Constable picked up a tattered piece of paper. Nope, it was a receipt from some down state sleaze store called Whips and Chains. Next, he found a receipt from another store. This store was named Leather and Bondage. These two receipts really got the Constable's attention.

The following month the Constable married Mrs. Gelhaven. The most noteworthy item, however, was the observation that Peter Bark Like a Dog relayed to The Horton Bay Gazette gossip columnist. The paper printed the news item that the newlyweds now burned all their trash in a rusted out fifty gallon drum placed at the back of their property. A year later Bark Like a Dog noted that even in a driving rain or on the coldest winter day both the Constable and his wife watched over the burning trash until it was completely reduced to ashes.

The paperwork on Mrs. Gelhaven's original crime of putting her trash in someone else's dumpster mysteriously was lost at the courthouse. All charges were dropped. The couple honeymooned in beautiful, downtown East Jordan.

Over the last 139 years the only person formally expelled from Horton Bay was the notorious Doctor Na Na. At first, locals in the bay felt that the doctor was a good person. His hobby, so it seemed, was to feed deer in his back yard. He would buy bags of corn and carrots at the General Store. Children used to congregate at his house around sundown to watch the herds of deer leave the sanctuary of the dense forest and amble towards the feed. During the summer months fudgies often stopped by with their cameras. It was a friendly, touching moment, and it was not unusual to see families, holding hands, as they watched a doe and fawn nibble on an ear of corn.

One night around three in the morning, the doctor's next door neighbor, Wilma Glassbrenner, got up to have a piece of the lemon meringue pie she had prepared the night before. She was looking out her kitchen window when she noticed a light in the doctor's house. She peered intently across the dark expanse of lawn and saw that a small herd of deer was feeding. She smiled and lingered for a moment to enjoy the scene. Then her eyes wandered back to the light in the window. It was then that she spotted what looked like a rifle barrel just peeking out of the curtains. Next, she heard a muffled popping noise. She blinked in surprise and turned in time to see a wonderful buck leap into the air and then fall dead, stretched across the feed pile.

Wilma gasped in horror. After about a minute she saw the doctor walk out his back door and grab the dead deer by the back hooves. The doctor slowly tugged the carcass across the lawn and into his garage.

Wilma was so shocked and petrified that she couldn't eat her pie. She sat in her darkened house for about an hour trying to convince herself that she had dreamed the entire affair. The next morning, however, she broke out in a cold sweat while she was having coffee at the General Store and she overheard the doctor invite the mayor over for some venison stew. Wilma could no longer control herself so she went to the phone and called the Constable.

The Constable conducted a thorough investigation, but in the end all the evidence was circumstantial and no arrest was made. People in the bay were quick to condemn the doctor. He was only another phoney environmentalist. It wasn't long before the General Store refused to sell the doctor corn and carrots. The fudgies stopped visiting his house. People shunned him on the street. He was a closet deer killer! The doctor's reputation was shot.

The doctor became a hermit, rarely leaving his house. Over the next several years he became very bitter. It wasn't long before he began sitting on his front porch taunting locals as they wandered by on their way to Horton Creek where they played water polo every afternoon. He'd sit on his porch and stick his thumbs in his ears and wiggle his fingers at children. Often he'd shout, "Na, Na, Na, Na." People in the bay were not amused. An emergency meeting was called and the City Council passed a secret ordinance that made it a crime to stick your thumbs in your ears, wiggle your fingers and shout Na, Na, Na ,Na.

The following day the Constable was waiting in a clump of trees when the doctor began his act. Of course, the doctor was found guilty. He was sentenced to one day in Hortontraz or given the option of receiving a suspended sentence in return for leaving Horton Bay. Not caring to do hard time in what locals lovingly called The Rock, The Stir, The Slam the doctor left town.

To this day locals keep a vigilant eye out for anyone with their thumbs in their ears, who wiggle their fingers and shout Na, Na, Na, Na. The Constable has thus far issued twenty eight citations for this infraction, and during the last election campaign vowed to run every perpetrator of this dastardly crime out of the village. During the campaign the Constable was quoted as saying, "These low lifes can go to East Jordan where this sort of thing is still tolerated."

71

Chapter Seven
Peter Bark Like a Dog

The weathered and laconic Indian had been a fixture in Horton Bay for as long as Mary Harris, the flamingo thief and oldest living resident, could remember. She remembered that he was already an old man when she was only a little girl. His bent figure could be seen silently walking through the woods. If he passed another person he would sometimes nod his head, but in his eyes it was easy to see that he possessed great knowledge.

Now, he was teased incessantly by the little summer brats, whose families owned fancy homes in the exclusive and gated Horton Bay Estates. The brats would be loitering around the General Store when Peter would amble by. As soon as they spotted him they all started barking like a pack of wild dogs. The brats jeered and howled, "Woof, woof, woof". Peter only ignored them. He was used to the abuse. He'd grown up with abuse as had the other proud members of the great Ottawa and Ojibway nations, the original residents of what is now Horton Bay.

The old Indian's family name had been Shaquajah. Years ago the government said that had to be changed in order to fit in with their scheme of things. The family was given a choice, either take the name Tom Smith or give yourself a name with English words. Bark Like a Dog seemed a lot more original than Smith. Now the brats, Johnny Smith, Mickey O'Roarty and Dick Gazzinya tagged after Peter hooting and hollering. Their parents sat on the General Store's front porch sipping their morning coffee and talking about the new stock offering in Horton Bay Tours, Ltd.. One big shot boasted that he could afford to buy five hundred shares of the new

72

offering. Like Peter, they ignored the children's barking.

Many of the thousands of researchers, who have flocked to Horton Bay over the years believe that the wild, ten foot tall beast, that is said to roam aimlessly through the dense forests around the village, is merely a legend concocted by Peter Bark Like a Dog's ancestors. The Indians called the creature Windigo. The researchers concluded that the Indians knew that such a myth would have been the ideal deterrent to the White settlers who were intent upon stealing all the land from the Grand River north into Canada. This is land that belonged to the Indian Nations. The Treaty of Paris ended the American Revolution. In this treaty the new congress recognized that much of what is now called Michigan rightfully belonged to the Indians. Squatters and settlers were forbidden from taking this land.

Everyone, including the new congress, ignored this provision. And so, the researcher's believe that the Indians invented a monster that would frighten off the White thieves. Windigo was said to be a hairy, smelly, eight hundred fifty pound monster, who devoured everything in sight. Surely the White man would flee in fear. At least that has been the researcher's opinion.

Peter Bark Like a Dog knew differently. His people knew the history of the land. They knew every tree, the wind, the sun, the mists and the shadows. Their love of their land was intense. They also knew every creek, every hill, every inland lake. They knew the great lake, every ridge, and every whisper in the trees. This was their land. Their history was never put into writing, but passed from generation to generation through stories. These stories told of Windigo. There was a Windigo. There still is.

Old as he was, Bark Like a Dog still went out at dusk every night in search of the elusive creature. He looked for signs in the woods; tracks in the loamy soil, hair rubbed off on tree trunks, broken branch twigs, the bones of some unfortunate fudgie. He knew that Windigo was out there, lurking on the outskirts of Horton Bay, watching and waiting. People thought that the old Indian was crazy because no one in the recent history of the bay had ever seen the beast. Oh, there had been drunken reports to the Constable that a hairy creature had been seen darting in and out of rush hour traffic on the Horton Bay Express. Nothing ever came of those supposed sightings except that once The Salamander was arrested for jaywalking. Even Ernest Hemingway wrote a short story about Windigo. His publisher rejected the story as "unbelievable". |The publisher instructed Hemingway to write a story that people could believe, so Hemingway wrote about a worn out old man who catches a 3,000 pound marlin on a hand line. That story won the Nobel Prize! No, most people thought that Windigo was only an Indian myth. That is, until the night of August twenty fifth, the night of the annual Farewell Party, a grand end of summer affair at Horton Bay Estates.

That night was a dark night, a very lonely night. The trees sighed with the breeze and every few minutes it sounded like a far away moan. It was a good night to stay inside and forget that the happy summer of swimming in the bay, another carefree summer in Horton Bay was at an end. The children played on the dock, the adults sipped their drinks. It was quiet for an end of summer party, but just then the silence was broken by the eerie wail, the forlorn screech of a beast that was on the prowl. Those revelers, who heard the wail, nervously and maybe a bit inadvertently, dismissed the sound as the tugging of a sailboat at her moorings or perhaps the whelp of an errant fox or bat or some meddlesome creature of the night. Bark Like a Dog knew differently. He had heard this sound before. He knew.

Bark Like a Dog was on the move. He crept through the underbrush, silently as his forefathers had taught him. Ahead, he saw the paper lanterns that ringed the Horton Bay Estates party. The multicolored light reflected on the water. He saw the innocent children on the dock, the adults hemming and hawing as they discussed their money. The creature bellowed again. This time everyone heard it. The sound hung in the thin night air. It hung there like a hangman's noose and the party grew silent. Everyone was in peril! A hush fell over the party. Bark Like a Dog knew what to do. He crept forward, barely breathing. He made not a sound. The adults at the party seemed to know that danger lurked just on the perimeter of the lantern's light. Mothers called to their frightened children. The men panicked. The monster moved closer to the circle of light. Later, witnesses say that they could smell the creature's breath. The mother's screams scared the children and in a matter of seconds everyone was running for the safety of the party room, a common area shared by all club members. The common room contained a whirlpool spa. Little did anyone realize that Windigo, the monster, the so called myth, loved a hot bubble bath every now and then.

When the beast broke through the solarium, adjacent to the spa, Pandemonium reigned. Grown men hid beneath the fake water fall. Mothers cradled their children. People could say what they wanted, maybe what they hoped to believe, that all was safe, that this was only a bad dream, but there was no denying the beast. Windigo was there. His breath smelled worse than the mayor's underwear. Windigo bellowed and roared.

74

He licked his ugly lips. He rushed recklessly into the party, saliva dripping form his angry mouth. People say that his eyes were on fire, red balls of brilliant light. He hunted and searched. His tongue flickered about. The rich folk made their getaway.

It was only Bark Like a Dog who knew what to do. The old Indian sat down on the ground, the ground that only the day before he had dutifully raked clean of a few early leaves. This was the land that had once been a part of his nation, and now he sang. He raised his voice to the sky with the hope that the beast would be satisfied. Bark Like a Dog sang a tune, one that had been a favorite in Horton Bay for a long time: On the Good Ship Lollipop. Apparently the monster's rage was quelled. Bark Like a Dog sang well into the night. In fact, there were five reported complaints to the Constable's office about the late night singing, and the next day the Constable was forced to issue Bark Like a Dog a citation for disturbing the peace. Later that same night, Mrs. Purebottom placed a 911 call, claiming that she'd seen a creature with blood shot eyes peeking into her window. It turned out to be The Salamander, who had gotten lost on his way back home from the Eager Beaver Tavern.

The next day the frightened townspeople were up in arms. They gathered in front of the Constable's house, but he was asleep so they moved to the General Store. Something had to be done. Windigo had to be captured. The village had to be made safe. Fire Chief LaBlance and his Search and Rescue team searched the Horton Bay Estates area. It was discovered that all twenty five pepperoni pizzas that had been ordered for the Farewell Party were gone. There were a few crumbs of burnt crust and mozzarella cheese, but that was all. The Constable arrived on the scene and questioned the children. After thirteen hours he came to the conclusion that the children had only eaten one of the pizzas. The other twenty four were unaccounted for. The Constable believed that the Windigo monster was a pizza fanatic! The Constable issued a warning to the people asking them not to travel in groups of less than forty, and not to order pizza to go from the General Store. He believed that there was safety in numbers.

Fire Chief Lablance organized a Windigo hunt. The creature had to be caught. It was Harvey Whippleman who convinced the Fire Chief that a live Windigo was better than a dead one. Harvey already had plans to make Windigo a star attraction of the new Horton Bay Circus in the Round. He knew that fudgies would ante up for the high price of a ticket to see a monster eating pepperoni pizza. Volunteers for the hunt were recruited. Truth be known, it was a pretty motley looking bunch. The

75

Constable carried a butterfly net, Ron and Ronrico Bobsey wore their trash can disguises, Mary Harris dressed herself as a pink, plastic flamingo, The Salamander showed up drunk and was sent home and Harvey Whippleman carried a piece of old pepperoni pizza that he'd found under his living room couch. He figured that the pizza was left over from the time when he'd spread Mrs. Gelhaven's trash on the floor. Fire Chief LaBlance borrowed a tranquilizer dart gun from the Octopus Park. A special cage was built. The Fire Chief designated some of the group to be "beaters". These people were to walk side by side through the woods carrying tin plates, which they were to bang with metal spoons. Their job was to herd Windigo towards the pepperoni pizza bait that the Constable had set inside the huge cage. Whippleman Plastics (a division of Horton Bay Tours, Ltd.) built a seven foot tall replica of a scantily clad female Windigo, which was also put inside the cage as an enticement.

The hunters broke up into their assigned groups and began scouring the woods. The din of clanging tin plates could be heard as far away as Charlevoix. The hunt quickly turned out to be a disaster. The Fire Chief somehow shot the mayor in the butt with the tranquilizer gun. The mayor slept for five days, which beat the Constable's record of sleeping for four days. When the mayor finally awoke he claimed to have no memory of the incident. He then spent five days at the Minkoff Institute in New York for observation. Mary Harris apparently got hungry and went inside the Windigo cage for the pepperoni pizza. When she picked up the slice she triggered the special Windigo siren. When the hunters arrived at the cage they discovered that Mary had already eaten the pizza so the hunt was called off. Then the Fire Chief noticed that the female Windigo decoy was missing. It wasn't in the cage. Two days later the Constable had a member of his ASS 9 Patrol sniff out the decoy. The fake bird was found curled up in bed with Shifty Con. Some folks believe that this was the true reason that Mrs. Purebottom closed her school for girls and moved to Las Vegas where she became a stripper. She was billed as Polly and Her Not So Purebottom.

One week following the Windigo hunt Horton Bay residents were awakened by blood curdling screams. Every night for the next several weeks the piercing screams plagued the village. Hysteria swept through the town. People took the maniacal screams as a sign that Windigo was not happy with the village and its attempt to hunt him down. A special meeting was held and the scared citizens offered suggestions as to how to appease the savage beast. Harvey Whippleman saw an opportunity here and promptly opened Whippleman Pizza. Everyone flocked to his pizza

76

parlor and ordered deluxe pepperoni pizzas. The terrified people then left the pizza on their front porch at night as an offering to Windigo. Every morning the people awoke to find that the pizza was gone. Not even a crumb or empty pizza box remained. That amounted to over two hundred pizzas a night, and proved to the people that Windigo truly did exist and that he had an enormous appetite. The screaming stopped and the joyous people became convinced that Windigo was once again happy.

Every night Peter Bark Like a Dog left his humble cabin in the woods and methodically collected the pizzas from each house in the bay. He then sold the pizzas back to Whippleman Pizza at a predetermined price. After he gave his throat a few days rest from the late night screaming, Bark Like a Dog's voice returned and he was able to negotiate a new contract with Harvey Whippleman. Bark Like a Dog now owns ten thousand shares in Horton Bay Tours, Ltd., which makes Mr. Big Shot from Horton Bay Estate's five hundred shares look rather puny.

It is hard to keep a great people down.

Chapter Eight
THE FOUNTAIN OF YOUTH

Every year millions of people from around the world flock to Horton Bay for the opening of the trout season. The Brookies are running! What excitement it is to see the masses swarming towards Horton Creek laden down with creels, fly rods and beer coolers! The occasion is great for Horton Bay's economy and every year the town gears up for the onslaught of money that will pour into its cash registers.

Udell Lingus and his wife Connie hadn't missed the opening day of trout season in fifty seven years. They were avid enthusiasts who enjoyed the fly fishing in Horton Creek better than the fishing anywhere else in the country. Udell and Connie enjoyed vacationing in Horton Bay and this particular summer they were staying at the brand new Horton Bay Inn, a posh, five star hotel that overlooked the bay and catered to high society types. Udell and Connie were especially impressed at how clean everything was at the inn. They noted with admiration the sign attached to the rusty chain link fence that surrounded the swimming pool which read: **FUDGIES AND TRUCK DRIVERS MUST SHOWER BEFORE ENTERING POOL.**

Udell felt comfortable with the other guests who stayed at the inn. Before he had retired Udell had worked at Murray's Deli on New York City's Upper East Side. At the Deli Udell's nick name had been Skinny and he was known as Skinny, the singing butcher. One time Mrs. Gloria Van Pelt, the famous soprano, stopped at Murray's and said, "Hey you, Skinny, give me two pounds of pastrami and trim the fat." Udell liked to sing the song COD FISH BALL, but he often changed the words. This day

78

he sang:

Come along and follow me, into Murray's Del-l-i
We will eat pastram-i-i at Murray's Del-l-i.
Hot dogs lined up in a row
Mustard and onions ready to go,
With prices so low we're almost free
At Murray's Del-l-i.

Mrs. Van Pelt was so impressed that she declared, "Hey you, Skinny, you ought to be starring on Broadway with a voice like that!"

Udell thought she was right, but he'd already been Skinny, the singing butcher, for over thirty years and he knew that it was too late to quit and star on Broadway. Still, he liked to dream that if he had his life to live over again he could be Skinny, the singing Broadway star. But, that was only a dream.

Udell worked a total of forty seven years at Murray's and probably never would have retired except that when Murray died the estate sold the building to a New Jersey firm that opened a peep show in the building. Udell stopped in one day and noticed that in the exact spot where the sauerkraut barrel had stood there was now a dirty post card display. The first peep show booth was located where the walk in cooler had been. He was about to leave in disgust when a man behind the counter asked him if he wanted to buy some tokens for one of the peep shows. Not wanting to be rude, Udell bought two dollars worth of tokens and entered the first booth. He put five tokens in the slot and a curtain immediately slid back across a glass frame revealing a naked man eating a lollipop. Just then the man from behind the counter, who had sold him the tokens, opened the door and asked Udell, "Want some company?" It was then that Udell wished more than ever before that he had been a famous Broadway star. He might even had been able to star opposite of Mrs. Van Pelt. Now that would have really been something!

Though they were well into their eighties Udell and Connie still made the trek far upstream on Horton Creek where the fishing, according to the professionals, has always been the best. The terrain grows quite rough upstream, and it is no easy hike even for a youngster in good shape. But, the Lingus' felt that the fishing was worth the effort, and so they struggled up and down steep hills, through dense woods, briars and drooping vines. Had poison ivy been allowed to grow in Horton Bay they would have had to contend with that, but fortunately sixteen years earlier the City Council had banned the plant.

The exact location of the springs, which gush uncontrollably out of the ground creating Horton Creek, is about a mile north of the Sand Man's cabin. The Sand Man is a hermit who lives with his trusted hunting dog, Sloth. Both the Sand Man and Sloth spend most of their days lounging around the cabin, which is why they have the names they have. The Sand Man didn't have to work. He struck it rich during the big gold rush on Horton Creek at the beginning of the century. Along with thousands of prospectors from all over the world, the Sand Man panned for gold. One day he removed an old log from the creek and discovered a ninety pound nugget of gold. He was rich beyond description. At first, he bought fancy cars and smoked big cigars. He began hanging out with all the high society types. He developed their air of superiority and walked around with his nose in the air. He was taught that it wasn't a good idea to hang around with anyone who didn't have money. After all, what could someone who had no money ever do for you? He took lavish trips around the world. He bought expensive clothes and joined the Horton Bay Country Club. He spent a lot of time at the club with his new found friends playing golf and gin rummy. He talked a lot about his money. Everyone at the club talked about their money. The women, who came from money, suddenly showed a new found interest in him. These were the very same women who previously wouldn't have given him a second look. Now, they flocked around him when he stood at the country club bar. The Sand Man thought these women were interesting, though he wondered why they spent so much of their time doing volunteer work. They were forever attending vacuous meetings on how to raise money for the Horton Bay Museum, the Horton Bay Philharmonic Orchestra, the Save the Horton Bay Skunk crusade. These women acted as though they were saving the world and, at first, this impressed the Sand Man.

One night the Sand Man's car ran out of gas. It was very late and in those days all the stations in Horton Bay closed at midnight. The Sand Man hiked to the nearest pay phone and began calling his country club friends. One after another they refused to get out of bed, dress and come pick him up. The Sand Man called twenty six people before his pocket change ran out. He slept in his car that night. The next morning he quit the country club and bought his dog, Sloth. He forgot about the country club women and realized how very bored and tired they all were. He realized that the only thing these women were really trying to raise in the community were their own profiles and self esteem. It was enough to make him ashamed of what he had almost become.

The Sand Man retired from the social scene and took to spending his days sleeping on his porch. He had had more than enough of high society, and he knew that he could always count on Sloth. The only person who ever visited the Sand Man was the Horton Bay undertaker. He stopped by once a week to see if the Sand Man was still alive. The undertaker would walk back to the cabin and thrust a mirror beneath the Sand Man's nose. So far, the Sand Man has just been sleeping.

Nobody has ever ventured north of the Sand Man's cabin to trout fish, but every year the crowds of trout fishermen have continued to grow and every year Udell and Connie have pushed further north in an attempt to find a quiet spot to fish. This particular year they moved north of the Sand Man's cabin. Both the Sand Man and Sloth were sound asleep when the Lingus' hiked by.

Udell and Connie slowly worked their way upstream. It was a pleasant day, though an unseasonably warm one. By the time they reached a bend in the creek, which was just a few hundred yards from the bubbling springs, they were both perspiring. Normally, they would hurriedly don their waders, put a fly on the line and step into the fast flowing water, which shimmered a bright silver in the early morning sunlight. But they were warm from the hike so they sat down in the lush grass and watched the sun rise in the sky. They listened to the birds, the rustle of a light breeze in the trees, the chirping of crickets, the humming buzz of honey bees, and they enjoyed the brilliance of the day. They didn't speak, but they both were thinking, realizing, that each wonderful year of trout fishing could very well be their last. And so they lingered for a moment, quietly basking in the glow of the day.

Udell gingerly tested the water with his hand. It was cold, but refreshing.

"I'm not going to wear my waders," he said, smiling at his wife.

"Oh, honey, be careful. The water is awfully cold."

"Yeah, but it feels good. It will help cool me down after our long walk. Besides if I get cold I'll put them on."

Udell got his fly rod put together and stepped into the water. He walked out into the stream until the water was knee high and swirled about his legs. He could feel the tug of the current. The creek bed was lined with rocks about the size of hen's eggs. The rocks were smooth, and in the shady parts of the creek the rocks were a dark green and slippery to walk on. Udell pulled line off his reel and worked it out onto the water. He stepped towards the far bank where the water pooled around a fallen tree. Suddenly, he lost his balance and fell into the water. He floundered

81

helplessly for a moment while the current carried him a few yards downstream. The icy water bubbled over his head and when he opened his eyes he was underwater and could see the creek bottom and the smooth, shiny rocks. He remembered thinking how pretty it was down there and how if he died he might like to come back as a Brook Trout.

The current pushed him closer to the bank where he managed to dig his feet into a sandy spot. He stood and looked around for his fly rod. It had become hung up on a bush that grew over the bank and stretched into the water. Connie was on the shoreline frantically trying to grab his arm. At last he took a few feeble steps towards her and collapsed onto a warm patch of sand. He was breathing heavily and felt very tired. Connie had wrapped her sweater about his shoulders and wiped his face with her head scarf. She was crying and kept asking him over and over whether or not he was okay. He stayed on his back and stared straight up at the sky. He watched a pattern of clouds move slowly from right to left. He felt strange, as though something was happening to his body. His skin tingled, but there was no pain. He had the distinct sensation of movement and speed, just as if his body had somehow been picked up and hurtled through the air.

Oh, my God!" Connie shrieked.

He turned his head and looked at her. "What is it?"

She only stared back at him, her eyes wide with shock.

"What is it?" Udell repeated. He sat up, suddenly feeling quite well.

"Udell...you're...you're," Connie stammered.

"I'm what?" Udell said springing to his feet. "Come on, tell me." he demanded. He stretched his legs. They felt strong. He felt good. His wife watched in amazement. "Well? What is it?"

"Udell, you're young."

"Young? Yeah, I'm eighty some odd years young!"

"No, I mean you look young. At least fifteen years younger."

"What in the world do you mean?" He was growing a bit impatient. "Look, I understand that you just had a bit of a shock when I fell into the water, but I'm fine. Really I am."

"I know you're fine. That's what I'm talking about. You look great."

"I'm dripping wet."

"I'm trying to tell you that you look years younger, wet or dry."

Udell looked at her intently for a moment. "Well," he began, "come to think of it I do feel pretty good. Say, do you have your compact with you. Let me see your makeup mirror."

Connie dug into her pack and found her small purse. "Here," she said, handing him the mirror.

Udell took the mirror from her and held it to his face. He gasped in astonishment. He was young! At least younger than he had been earlier. He studied himself intently. By God! He appeared to be a good fifteen years younger.

"What in the world has happened to me?" he asked.

Connie stepped forward and gently stroked his face. She let her fingers slowly trace the contours around his nose and mouth. "There's no doubt about it," she finally announced. "You are younger. Something has happened to you that has made you younger."

Udell puffed up his chest, feeling the air fill his lungs. He let out his breath and felt good. He could feel the strength surge through his body. Now he lifted his right arm and made a muscle. Connie squeezed his bicep and marveled at the size of the muscle.

They looked at each other in wonder. Then they let their eyes move to Horton Creek. "The water!" they both said at once. They looked at each other again.

"No, it couldn't be,"Udell said evenly. "How could that be?"

"I don't know, but there is no denying it. Something has happened to make you take years off your appearance."

Udell looked into the mirror again. "Yeah," he mumbled. "It's not our imaginations is it?"

Connie touched his face again. "This is no illusion," she said, patting his cheek.

"But do you really think that the water did this to me?"

"What else could it be? You were an old man when you stepped into the creek. Then you slipped and fell. You went under water and after only being out of the water for a few minutes the years just started melting away."

"The Fountain of Youth!" Udell screamed in delight. "We've discovered the Fountain of Youth!" He jumped around in an excited little dance.

"It must be true!" Connie said happily.

"There's only one way to find out." Udell looked at his wife. "You have to get in the water."

"Oh, Udell, I'm afraid."

"Don't you want to take years off your life? Don't you want to be young again? This is what people have been searching for since the beginning of time."

"You're right! We can both be forever young. We can have it all." She stepped hurriedly towards the creek. She turned and gave one last, long look at her husband and then dashed into the water. She felt the icy tingle as the water crept up about her breast. She immediately felt her breasts rise and grow firmer, more taut. She dunked herself underwater and held her breath for as long as she could. She too felt a lifting sensation and the sense of being moved rapidly almost as though she were looking out the window of a speeding train and watching the landscape rush by. Finally she burst to the surface of the water and took a big breath of air. She bounced out of the water and sat down of the bank.

Udell ran to her side and looked at her. He studied her for a moment. His eyes grew big with amazement. His wife was young again. She looked as if she was once again forty five years old. But, she was eighty five. Udell rubbed his eyes and looked at his wife again. It was real. She was younger!

They both plunged into the water and took another thirty second soak. When they emerged they were approximately thirty eight years old.

"Wow!" Udell whispered in amazement as he studied his wife. He pumped up his left bicep and felt it with his right hand. He was a strong, young man again. "We have to be careful, Connie. We were only in the water for a few minutes and look how young we are."

"I'm going back in for another treatment," Connie said excitedly.

Udell grabbed her by the arm. "Hold on there, sweetie. We don't want to take off too many years."

"Why not?" Connie asked.

"Well," Udell said thoughtfully, "we don't know if there are any side affects. We need to be cautious."

"We're young again, Udell. What's there to be cautious about? We can be forever young."

"I still say we need to go slowly. Besides we can always come back to the springs and take another swim. We'll just keep this as our little secret."

"Secret! Udell! We've discovered the Fountain of Youth. We can be rich! Forever young and forever rich!

What do we do?"

"We'll contact that successful business man, you know, the one who won the Horton Bay Entrepreneur of the Year award for the last sixteen years."

"Harvey Whippleman!" Udell almost yelled.

84

"Exactly! He'll know how to help us start our Fountain of Youth business and market our discovery."

By ten o'clock the next morning Harvey had bought the land just north of the Sand Man's hut. Harvey now owned the Fountain of Youth. He persuaded Udell and Connie to sign on as Co-Publicity Directors, which meant that they would stand in front of the ticket counter showing off their new, younger bodies. Harvey made arrangements for life size pictures of Udell and Connie, when they were eighty five, to be positioned in front of the ticket counter. A sign over the pictures read: **BEFORE**. Udell and Connie stood beneath another sign that read: **AFTER**. Business was booming. Everyone wanted to be young again. Everyone except the Sand Man. He thought being young was a drag. He preferred sleeping in his hammock on the front porch, which, as he said, is all he did when he was young. His dog, Sloth, proved not to be so faithful after all. Sloth took a secret fifteen minute dip one night after the fountain was closed. The next day he ran rabbits through the woods for nine hours. The Sand Man claimed that the dog was ruined and sold him to Harvey. Sloth is now one of the famed bank surveillance dogs and has been renamed, Big Duke.

Harvey was deathly afraid of lawsuits. He'd learned a long time earlier to charge a huge price, but only give the customer a little bit. He realized (he only need look at the Lingus') that too much exposure to the Fountain of Youth could be disastrous. This is why for the first time since forming Horton Bay Tours, Ltd. Harvey decided to spend some money on product research. He hired a company out of Alpena that specialized in researching fountains of youth. Harvey had read about the firm in a tabloid while waiting in the check out at the General Store.

Manfried Wilhelm, the Executive Director of the Sears Youth Foundation, reported to Horton Bay and began what was to turn into a six year study of the Horton Creek springs. At the end of the study Dr. Wilhelm presented his report to Harvey and The Horton Bay Gazette, whom Harvey had invited to the meeting for publicity purposes. Dr. Wilhelm discovered that approximately ten miles beneath the springs there are thousands of miles of honeycombed limestone chambers. Using sonar testing, Dr. Wilhelm concluded that the honeycomb chambers are not man made. At least, not man made by man as we know him. The pattern was laid out in what Dr. Wilhelm believed to be some sort of map. His report speculates that the chambers were constructed by extraterrestrials. He proposed that a division of his company, Extraterrestrial Studies and Sightings conduct another study. Harvey declined this suggestion, but, as The Horton Bay Gazette reported some two months later, Dr. Wilhelm's company and all its subsidiaries are now wholly owned by Horton Bay Tours, Ltd.

Dr. Wilhelm's report did conclusively prove that the Horton Bay Fountain of Youth removes one year for every one minute of soaking, give or take a few months. The report also stated that for best results all clothes should first be removed. Harvey immediately opened the Horton Bay Nudist Colony adjacent to the springs, but after a special meeting of the City Council, it was voted that nudity not be allowed in the bay The only councilperson who voted in favor of the nudist colony was Miss Purebottom, who lately had taken to going braless and wearing a lot of eye makeup.

Udell Lingus soon began to enjoy fame in Horton Bay. Every day he would take a short soak in the Fountain of Youth. It wasn't long before he was twenty three years old. It was then that he took up arm wrestling, body building, sumo wrestling and competitive bubble gum bubble blowing. He became very accomplished in all these sports. Sumo wrestling and bubble gum bubble blowing quickly became his favorites. He worked diligently to master each sport. Eight hours a day he would practice sumo wrestling, specializing in the Soo Wa style, which translates to fire and water. In the beginning he worked out with the Horton Bay University wrestling team, but he quickly outgrew this competition. Udell searched throughout Horton Bay for wrestling partners.

Then he had a spectacular idea. Probably the most famous sporting event in Horton Bay is the annual Run for the Slop pig race. This race is considered the jewel of the national pig racing circuit. Every year the town prepares for the moment when thousands of cheering fans will here the starter's gun and dozens of pigs ridden by the country's best jockeys will thunder down Main Street in a cloud of dust and a hearty oink, oink, oink! The Horton Bay race is considered by experts to be the most demanding race in the country. As a result many trainers work their thoroughbred pigs rigorously. Udell had noticed that a local pig, and last year's winner, Hog Wash, was working on strength conditioning with another pig named, Pig Out. Udell asked the trainer if he could start wrestling the pigs. The trainer thought it was a fabulous idea.

Every morning crowds gathered at the pig's work out sessions, eager to see Udell wrestle a pig. Udell and the pig's were evenly matched and sometimes the matches lasted a full hour before someone would cry uncle. After about a month of working out with the pigs Udell began to get the upper hand. He had learned the pigs best moves and was now able to pin them within fifteen minutes. It was at this point when Udell invented

86

what has now become known as the Twisted Pretzel Banana Split Move, which purists claim is merely a variation of the Japanese move named, Spitting on the Dragon. With this move Udell was able to put the pigs in a great deal of pain. The pig's trainer said enough was enough and refused to let them wrestle any more. Connie, who was acting as Udell's trainer announced that Udell was prepared to sign for a match with Japan's most famous sumo wrestler, Ogura Sakitome. Udell, only weighed one hundred fifteen pounds. This is small for a sumo wrestler, but Udell, whom the Japanese called Tiny Buttocks, was extremely fast. Tiny also had a terrific tolerance for pain. The match would be broadcast on pay for view by Horton Bay Tours, Ltd. Harvey billed the match as a grudge match, claiming that Tiny had called the four hundred twenty pound Sakitome "fatso." For his part, Sakitome was supposed to have called Udell, "Sashi, Sashi," which is worst kind of wimp in Japan.

Udell took a short soak in the Fountain of Youth. He wanted to keep his age at twenty three. Then he took off for Japan. The match was watched by millions of people world wide including every single Horton Bay resident except the Sand Man, who was asleep at the time. The match lasted five hours and twenty six minutes. At that point Tiny had Sakitome in the dreaded arm pit hold and the Japanese wrestler submitted. Later, the Japanese government vigorously protested, stating that Tiny had failed to use a deodorant before the fight. Tiny left Japan and signed a deal with Spell Bound, the leading men's deodorant in Horton Bay.

Udell spent his free time blowing bubble gum bubbles. This sport has been a favorite in Horton Bay for many years. It all started when the General Store received a double shipment of Big Boy bubble gum. The gum was featured at an end of summer sale price and locals started buying. People sat on the store's wide front porch chewing and blowing bubbles. Pretty soon the competitive nature of the chewers began to show. People stuffed more and more pieces of gum in their mouths and struggled to see who could blow the biggest bubbles. The store sponsored a Labor Day bubble blowing contest, which attracted ninety seven contestants and thirty five hundred spectators. From that humble beginning bubble gum bubble blowing has become a very big sport.

Today the sport involves three bubble categories spread over a men's, women's and children under twelve divisions. The categories are size, shape and artistic expression. Udell excelled in the size category. He claimed that his twenty three year old lungs had the strength necessary to blow the really big ones. It wasn't long before he was winning so many amateur tournaments that he decided to turn professional. He also conducted many clinics in the bay. He always chewed the grape flavor gum and when autograph hounds sought him out locals would tell them to look for the guy with the purple ring around his mouth.

Just when it seemed that everything in Udell's and Connie's life was perfect disaster struck. Connie couldn't get enough of the Fountain of Youth. She simply wanted to be younger and younger. She had become obsessed with being young. Every day she studied her face and body in the mirror. Then she'd head for the Fountain of Youth for another soak. It wasn't long before she was listening to rock music and subscribing to teen magazines. Udell first noticed that something was amiss when Connie took a new interest in hop scotch and Barbie dolls. Then one day she jumped into the Fountain of Youth and paddled around for a full hour, which is well beyond the recommended exposure to the water. Fortunately, another customer spotted Connie, who was now a wailing infant and unable to swim, floundering in the water. The child was plucked from the water and returned to Udell.

Initially, Udell was furious. Here he was a robust twenty three year old man stuck with a crying infant. He especially hated having to change Connie's diapers. He hired Olga, a Swedish nanny to care for Connie and do some cooking for the household. One evening Udell returned home from a bubble gum bubble blowing exhibition and discovered a huge pot of Swedish stew bubbling on the stove. He took a large spoon and stirred the stew, noticing the large chunks of beef. Dinner wouldn't be served for another hour and he was hungry so he decided to sneak a bite or two. The first bite tasted awful. Olga was supposed to have been a better cook. After all, she had presented herself with impeccable credentials. Udell added some salt and pepper, stirred and tried another bite. Just then Olga entered the kitchen.

"Mr. Lingus!" she exclaimed. "What are you doing?"

"I was just trying your Swedish stew, Olga and I'm sorry to tell you that this stuff tastes like shit!"

"That's because it is! I'm boiling Connie's diapers in that pot."

Udell was so upset over this turn of events that he eventually filed a lawsuit against Horton Bay Tours, Ltd. charging that the firm failed to adequately warn customers about the capabilities of the anti- aging water. The suit was finally settled out of court when Harvey Whippleman offered a scholarship to Connie to his day care company, Happy Critters. Udell visited the day care facility and was satisfied when he saw Connie was quite happy playing patty cake with the other children. Udell began dating one of the groupies who followed the sumo wrestling circuit. He stayed out late at night, drank too much and began to be a regular at the Horton Bay disco scene. It wasn't long before he grew weary of this and longed to be an old man again.

The memory of sitting quietly on the bank of Horton Creek, listening to the gentle gurgle of water as it swirled around a fallen branch, holding his wife's frail hand and watching the western sky turn a soft salmon color seemed to him to be the most important thing in the world.

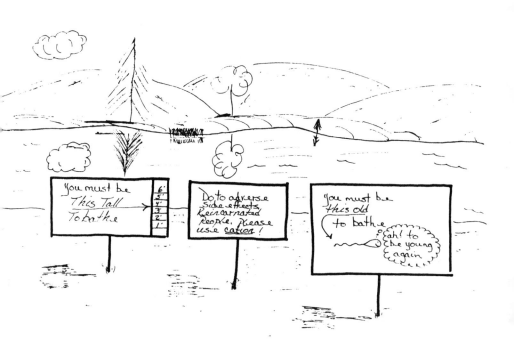

Chapter Nine
HORTIE, THE HORTNESS MONSTER

The water in Horton Bay is very deep. Very deep, indeed. In fact, oceanographers in mini subs have dived in the bay for years trying to determine the exact depth. The equipment and depth meters routinely stopped functioning properly at a depth of three miles below the surface. At that depth there is no sunlight and the mini subs illuminate the darkness with their high power halogen lamps. What they saw was a different world, stranger than any Japanese science fiction movie. The two man crews of these deep diving subs returned with amazing stories of an eerie under water world in Horton Bay. While sun bathers lolled about on rubber rafts and children paddled about leisurely in the gentle surf it was discovered that several miles below an incredible seventy foot monster prowled the dark water. The monster had enormous wing like fins that propelled it at amazing speeds through the water. One scientist gauged that the monster was capable of swimming at speeds in excess of two hundred miles an hour. When the huge monster flapped it's fins the back wash nearly destroyed the mini sub. It was evident that this monster ruled the bay.

For years the existence of the Horton Bay monster was kept secret. The Horton Bay City Council sealed the oceanographer's report in the Town Hall safe, which really only consisted of a cigar box that was hidden on the ledge above the broom closet. This document referred to the Monster as Hortense in honor of Councilwoman, Sarah Ledbelly's mother. Before long the members of the City Council shortened the name to Hortie, the Hortness Monster. Hortie was secretly discussed at many of the meetings. Many on the council wanted to destroy the monster so that the bay would be safe. They discussed dropping huge depth charges in the bay at night while the townspeople slumbered. Someone proposed taking Horton Bay's nuclear sub out of dry dock (the sub had been in dry dock since East Jordan had surrendered in the fudgie war of 1912). It was thought that the nuclear sub had the speed and technology necessary to trap the monster in the shallows where Horton Creek flows into the bay.

There the sub could fire nuclear torpedos at the swimming serpent. The City Council feared that if word of the monster got out then the important fudgie business would rapidly dwindle. In the end it was decided to leave the monster alone since the monster had never bothered anyone in the bay. Hortie would remain a secret and the tranquil life in Horton Bay would continue as before. But then Harvey Whippleman found out about Hortie. He had been wandering around City Hall late one night looking for a cigar when he spotted the box over the broom closet door. He knew immediately that the monster's existence had to be made public. He reasoned that fudgies from all over the world would flock to Horton Bay to see a real live sea monster. Harvey had to use the Freedom of Information Act in order to have the oceanographer's report released to the Horton Bay Gazette. The report stunned the nation, not to mention the locals.

Panic and fear reigned supreme in the bay. The beaches were deserted, the white clapboard cottages shuttered against the perceived terror of Hortie, the Hortness Monster. Harvey Whippleman made a killing selling Hortie souvenirs. There were tiny sea serpent monsters carved from Petoskey and Horton Creek stones. Tee shirts and sweat shirts were big sellers, as was the Hortie doll. The Whippleman Amusement Park with the state of the art Hortie roller coaster. The General Store even got involved, offering a Hortie-sicle and Hortie burger. The people gradually learned to live with the daily fear that a huge monster lurked in the dark depths of Horton Bay. Eventually, the sunbathers and swimmers slowly returned. Jet and water skiers scooted back and forth across the bay. People enjoyed themselves and Hortie mania dissipated, the way the morning sun burns off the fog in the Horton Bay swamp.

One August afternoon a fudgie named Miles Huffington III, from somewhere downstate, was swimming in the bay with his wife and two children. Miles had pulled his 100 foot motor launch into Horton Bay and was swimming off her large swim platform. The motor launch had become the talk of the bay, spectacular and gleaming with what appeared to be a thousand pounds of polished teak. Miles was rich and loved showing off his money. He wasn't very well liked in the bay. His yacht held enough fuel to support two or three poor families for an entire year. Miles loved to fill up her tank, but rarely gave anything to charity. That was what welfare was for, he often said whenever he expounded on his philosophy of life at boozy dinner parties.

The family frolicked in the water when suddenly, the water in the bay grew agitated. The waves rolled into the beach with greater force.

91

The water heaved as giant swells pounded in from the deeper water. The shallow beach water became turbid when the waves rolled in and frightened people fled, shrieking as they sought the safety of the upper dunes. The people huddled together and pointed out to the middle of the bay where the water seemed to boil. The Huffington family was caught in the large, undulating swells. Miles shouted to his wife and kids to swim to the yacht. It was a dreadful scene. The youngest child disappeared under water. The wife screamed in sheer desperation as she tried to swim to her child, but the strong waves pushed her back. Miles grabbed her from behind and pulled her to the yacht. The other child had climbed on board and thrown a life preserver in the direction of his missing brother. The yacht pitched violently as if she were a play toy in the palm of some powerful, invisible hand. The parents clung to each other as they climbed aboard. The swells now crashed over the stern. Miles grabbed his family and lashed them all to the helm. They stared in disbelief as the gigantic sea serpent surfaced, sending sprays of water one hundred feet in the air.

It was Hortie! And there on Hortie's back was the missing child, laughing and shouting as he rode the monster like a cowboy rides a wild Brama bull. The serpent thrashed it's long tail once and, like a rocket, propelled itself across the bay. Two magnificent fins on either side of the monster acted like rudders as the monster turned abruptly and sped out to the main body of Lake Charlevoix. The people on the yacht and the beach watched in horror as the monster and child disappeared. No one had comprehended that the monster and child were only playing a game.

And then they were back, alongside the yacht. The boy stepped from the monster's back to the yacht. The monster panted like a tired dog and smiled. The sea serpent had had a wonderful time.

"It's okay," the boy shouted enthusiastically. "Hortie's my friend! She just wants to be friends."

Very tentatively, the others approached the monster. Suddenly, Hortie gave them all a quick lick with her long, serpent tongue.

"She's only giving you a kiss," the boy screamed with glee. "Hortie calls it giving sugar!"

Harvey Whippleman signed Hortie to a long term contract. She performed every afternoon at the Octopus Park show. In return Harvey had to bring a picnic dinner down to the bay and once a week the two would share a delightful meal, often listening to the mellifluous sounds of the Horton Bay Trio. Hortie loved good music and insisted that whenever the trio was not on the road that they play at the picnics. Harvey brought tapes for the times when the trio was out of town.

Hortie very quickly became a featured attraction in the bay. Her picture was plastered on post cards, posters, coffee mugs, calendars and just about everything that Whippleman Graphics could purchase through the Whippleman Import Division. Everyone loved Hortie and it seemed as if the public couldn't get enough of her. She had many, many visitors to the new deep water dock the city built just for her. She attended all the ribbon cutting ceremonies that took place on the water. She actually used her giant tail to break ground when the City Council voted to dig a canal between the bay and Walloon Lake. Hortie had it all, but she was still lonely.

Harvey sensed that something was amiss and began taking out want ads in the Personals section of The Horton Bay Gazette. Just maybe, there was another sea monster out there, a male sea monster. Two weeks after Harvey began running the ads he had a response, but it turned out to only be a prank. It was his pal, The Salamander, who claimed that his name gave him first rights to Hortie. Finally, Harvey gave up with the ads. By now, Hortie was beginning to show her loneliness. Her weight dropped off by some three thousand pounds. She had a somewhat gaunt look about her face and she seemed sluggish during the Octopus Park shows. Harvey hated to spend the money, but he wasn't about to let his star attraction die of a lonely heart so he sent an emergency cable to Scotland. The reply stated that Lord Stanley Lochie, better known as the Lochness monster would be willing to visit Hortie for a fee of five hundred thousand dollars. Harvey was outraged! He ranted about the bay for a full two days before he had the money wire transferred to Lord Lochie's account in Glasgow.

Lord Lochie and Hortie hit it off from the beginning, so well that Lord Lochie promised a return visit for no charge. Hortie was estatic, and also pregnant! Harvey was beside himself with joy. Just think, he told the locals, who gathered at the General Store, a baby sea monster! The Horton Bay Morals Society was not so pleased. They thought an unmarried Hortie would be nothing but an embarrassment and a bad example for the young people. Harvey had the same person who had forged the phoney documents for the illegal immigrants that made them either locals or natives make up a wedding certificate, which he had framed and presented to the old bags who chaired the Morals Society. They were pleased enough to send Hortie and Lord Lochie a wedding gift.

It wasn't long before Hortie's gynecologist discovered that Hortie was putting on more weight than expected! At first, it was suspected that the Horton Bay Gourmand Club had been slipping Hortie some culinary delights, but a closer physical examination revealed that the lower abdominal swelling was a result of Hortie expecting twins! This news really sent shock waves reeling through the bay. The locals decorated their cottages with pink and blue ribbons, the General Store began selling the Hortie burger as a "two for the price of one"special and The Horton Bay Gazette sponsored a name the twins contest.

Fifteen months after Lord Lochie left town Hortie delivered her twins. The tiny infant sea serpents weighed six thousand pounds each at birth. They were given a vitamin B shot and some Taco Heaven burritos. Fudgies were subsequently advised not to feed the infants any food from Taco Heaven because it gave the twins a bad case of gas.

The boy girl twins were named Hortmon and Horticia. Congratulations from around the world poured into the bay. The twins are grown now and Lord Lochie visits his family once a year. Hortie is fine and still the number one attraction in the bay. Harvey Whippleman is currently filming a documentary on Hortie's life, which when completed will be for sale at $299.99.

Two Short Stories

THE LAST FRONTIER

Ben Adams had been feeling pretty low, but then again, it seemed he was always down about something. His worries had finally descended upon him with the same crushing finality as the grave digger's last few shovelfuls of dirt. It was then that he decided it was no longer possible to idly endure life, but that it was his time to die.

At age forty six it was difficult for him to remember the last time he'd been happy, truly happy, but especially since the divorce he'd been more depressed than usual. Following his divorce he gradually withdrew from the handful of people he considered friends. In reality they were only acquaintances, not friends. He understood this, which only served as another reminder that there was nothing worthwhile, nothing meaningful in his life. He just shut himself away, confused and wondering why life had to be so awfully painful. He had spent so much time recently asking himself why on earth he continued to endure this misery.

He'd always been a heavy drinker, but now he drank all the time. He fretted over the state of world affairs, and it was nothing for him to break into tears while sipping a cocktail and watching the evening news. Viewing the dreadful television scenes of an apartment fire that tragically claimed the lives of five children was almost more than he could bear, and justification for at least half a dozen more drinks. Yet, he never felt truly sorry for himself, only puzzled as to why even a modicum of happiness in life had eluded him.

He had been more angry than hurt when his wife calmly explained that she had fallen head over heels in love with another woman. Another woman! Why, he thought, did life have to be so awfully complicated. He understood that this was the nineties and in many circles may be acceptable behavior, but, by God, this was the love of his life, the only person who had blunted the constant undertone of pain he harbored over simply making it from one day to the next. And now, she'd fallen in love with her secretary! He didn't consider that this might be the result of some failing on her part, or possibly the fulfillment of natural urges. No, her leaving had to be his fault, and in his mind equaled the deep seated rejection he felt upon learning that he'd been adopted.

He loved his adopted parents more than anything in the world, yet he carried a fear of abandonment so real that it might as well have been a length of heavy chains coiled around his neck. When his parents did die prematurely in an auto wreck he saw their deaths as another case of people running out on him. Oh, why should a person be forced to live such a life! He'd considered all the arguments against suicide and once, he'd even called a suicide prevention hot line, but in the end he knew full well that this was something he had to do. He simply had grown weary of his life. He figured that if not happiness then at least peace would be his reward.

He took a gulp of his vodka and sighed heavily, relieved that he'd managed to make this decision. Immediately, he felt a sense of well being and security, the same sensation one has upon returning home from a very long journey. He knew from the start how the job would be handled. This knowledge, if not the actual decision, had rested in the recesses of his mind for quite a while. When his father died Ben had discovered an old Smith and Wesson revolver hidden in a shoe box at the back of his father's bedroom closet. The gun and a handful of bullets had been carefully wrapped in an oily rag.

He pulled himself from the chair and anxiously got the gun from a dresser drawer in his bedroom. He returned to his chair and drink, all the time staring at the gun. He held in his hand all that was needed to end the hurt. He took a deep breath and he could feel his heart pounding, the throb of the beat hammering in his temples. He hesitated, glancing through the front window. The slanting sun flickered through the budding spring leaves of the large maple trees. The house wouldn't do. He didn't like the idea of blood splattered over the walls and furniture. It may have only been a modest home, but he remembered that there had been some happiness there. The yard was no better. Over the past fourteen years he'd barely said more than a few words to his neighbors so the thought of them finding his body was distasteful.

He decided that finding the proper location would require some careful thought. He set the revolver on the table and very tiredly pulled himself to his feet. He walked to the sliding glass door and looked out at the sagging wood deck, and then past the gravel driveway at the burgeoning landscape that followed the curve of the road to Charlevoix. To his left the crooked branches of the apple tree his wife had planted showed the beginning light green fuzz of blossoms. He closed his eyes and remembered how his wife had baked pies with the moist, ripe fruit from the tree. The tree could be seen from the upstairs bathroom window, and in the autumn there had been nights when he had gotten up and seen deer, illuminated only by a fragile, pale moonlight, eating the apples that had fallen to the ground. Sometimes, he would wake his wife and together they would silently watch with a child's amazement as the deer fed.

He returned to his chair and sat down heavily. Yes, he decided, he must leave this place with all its memories. There had to be somewhere nearby where he could simply die, alone and surrounded by the cold starkness of the unfamiliar.

He did his best thinking with the stereo playing and a drink in his hand. He went to the kitchen and fixed himself another drink. Back in the family room he thumbed through the compact disc file. His eyes fell upon a CD by a little known group called DA YOOPERS, this name being a take off on the Scandinavian pronunciation of Michigan's upper peninsula, the U.P. Ben's house was less than an hour's drive from the U.P. Frequently in the past he had escaped to this remote region for a little solitude. If he enjoyed traveling at all he had to admit that he thrilled to crossing the Mackinac Bridge, which spans the Straits of Mackinac, the water that joins Lakes Michigan and Huron. The bridge was a conduit to some of the most spectacular and primitive land in the country.

Ben listened to the first song, THE LAST FRONTIER, and instantly hit upon the idea that he would kill himself in the U.P. And why not? It was remote, and either tranquil or violent depending on the weather. It was the perfect place to visit for a day or two, reflect upon his agony and then die.

That night he was unable to sleep. It was one of those dreadful nights when no matter how much he tossed and turned and plumped his pillow, it was impossible to find a comfortable position. These were the nights when he knew he hadn't had enough to drink, the nights he had come to accept as punishment for the innumerable failures and bitter disappointments in his life. As the long, dark hours wore on he drifted between the worlds of sleep and awake. The sleep was fitful with the distorted nightmares of a person with a high fever. When awake his thoughts were even worse. This was a time to recall every lost opportunity, and he did this in chronological order and in great detail. It was then that he thought of his shabby career and lost loves. He remembered his first love and then his parents. He remembered his wife and now tortured himself with imagined scenes of her in bed with her secretary. And then there was his only brother, who borrowed a large sum of money from him with the promise to repay in a couple of months. Two months later he skipped town and he hadn't heard from him since. God, it was more than a soul should bear! What a lonely night, and had it not been for his decision to end it all in the U.P. he probably would have rushed to the dresser for the revolver. He was thankful when a dull grey light shuddered in the eastern sky before turning pink and filling the room with a pale light, though daybreak did nothing to dispel his uneasiness or pain.

He packed a simple overnight bag, carefully tucking the revolver between the underwear and socks. He glanced at his house and yard and then without remorse drove through Petoskey, Pellston and the other towns along the way to the Mackinac Bridge. It was a beautiful, clear day and the water on either side of the bridge was the same deep blue as the sky. There was a gusting wind and a light chop on the water. In the distance he spotted a ferry headed for St. Ignace. He could make out passengers on the bow, leaning over the railing. There were wide eyed, happy children, secure in the circle of their parent's arms. Everyone on board waved. They waved to the land, to the sky, to the sea gulls overhead and to the irradiant wake that fell away from the boat. They were all on a journey, a pleasant journey filled with expectation. The swells were larger than the chop indicated because the ferry threw off an enormous spray each time her bow dug into a wave. The water looked cold, and, indeed, it would be a good six weeks before sail boarders and jet skiers would criss-cross the vista.

He decided his destination would be the miniscule town of Grand Marais on Lake Superior's southern shore. He chose this location because someone had mentioned that the town was a picturesque place with the rugged, raw magnificence of the true wilderness. The acres of pristine forests and miles of rolling sand dunes surrounding Grand Marais offered the ideal place to die. His body very well might never be found, and this was his desire. He could truly just disappear in the last frontier. This thought brought a contented smile to his lips.

In Seney, Michigan he turned right. Twenty five miles of desolate road and then Grand Marais and the lake. He guessed there wouldn't be any cops on such a forgotten stretch of road, and so what if he did get a ticket? He pushed the accelerator down and cruised at eighty. The cold, early spring air rushed in his window with a whoosh. When he neared the lake the air chilled by a good ten degrees, but it felt and smelled so good he left the window down. Both sides of the road were lined with dense forests of hardwood and hemlock. Once he crossed the Sucker River a loamy swale paralleled the road for several hundred yards. A few puffy clouds sagged heavily in the sky, their bellies tinged a dark grey. When Ben drove through the clouds' shadow the air smelled like a storm.

When he arrived in Grand Marais he immediately located a motel overlooking the deserted harbor. Even during the height of summer only a few boats would moor in the harbor and a handful of intrepid swimmers would dot the beach. This was north country and Ben felt good here.

After checking into the motel he headed for the nearest bar. There were only two in town and one wasn't open until after Memorial Day. He needed several stiff drinks, and time to sift through his thoughts. Tomorrow was time enough to explore and find a place to end it all. It had actually become that simple.

He headed down the empty street towards the bar. A cold wind whipped in from the lake and he drew his jacket tight at his throat. When he stepped into the bar it was warm and smelled of hamburgers and garlic. His face flushed in the sudden warmth. The place was quite crowded for three in the afternoon, but then he'd heard that hard core drinking was part of the U.P. life style. He took a seat at the bar and ordered a vodka on the rocks.

The bartender returned and placed the drink on the bar. "This one's on the house."

"What for?" Ben asked, somewhat puzzled.

"Well, it's not really on the house. That guy down there is buying everyone a drink today." The bartender pointed at a wrinkled, old man at the far end of the bar.

"But he doesn't know me," Ben protested, putting one hand up, the palm facing the bartender.

"Doesn't matter," the bartender replied, ignoring Ben's outstretched hand. He slid the drink across the bar. "He's celebrating today and everyone who comes into the place gets one free drink."

"What's he celebrating?" Ben asked.

"He got his limit of perch today."

"That's it?"

"That's it. We have simple fun up here, but we enjoy ourselves. Willy's real tickled with himself 'cause he's got a secret spot where he goes on the lake for catching perch. He's been the only one to catch his limit this

101

year."

Ben waved at Willy, and catching his eye hollered down the length of the bar, "Thanks for the drink, Willy, and congratulations!"

Willy grinned from ear to ear and then began chuckling so hard that his entire body shook and his face turned red. At last he took a swallow of his beer and waved back. He picked up a hard boiled egg from a napkin in front of him and waved it at Ben. "Want an egg?"

"No thanks," Ben shouted back, and then he asked the bartender, "are those pickled eggs he's eating?"

"Yeah," the bartender answered, pointing to a huge jar of eggs on the back bar, "and they give you the farts."

"I'll stick to my vodka."

Someone put money into the antiquated jukebox and a couple started dancing. The song was a fast tune and they danced a cross between a polka and a jitter bug. Two more couples joined the dancing for the second song. Everyone seemed to know each other, which was only natural considering the size of the town. It was a pleasant gathering and Ben felt at ease. The drinks were sliding down and he relaxed, allowing himself to get caught up in the heady atmosphere. He swiveled his bar stool around so that he could watch the dancing.

A woman, perhaps in her early thirties, emerged through the half shutter doors separating the bar and the kitchen. She carried a huge tray of pizza to a group at a table near the door. The woman had jet black hair that fell to her shoulders, pale blue eyes and the palest, milky white skin Ben had ever seen. He stared at the woman. There was something about her looks and the way she moved that intrigued him. When she walked by a table at the far end of the bar she stopped and smiled as she spoke to a group of older women. Ben noticed that she tipped her head from one side to the other as she spoke, and as she did her black hair bounced about her face. He watched her as she moved across the room. All at once, he found himself thinking about what her breasts must look like. He imagined that they would be absolutely white and smooth, with nipples so pale they barely held any color. The woman noticed him staring at her and smiled. Ben awkwardly looked away and turned back to the bar. He motioned to the bartender for another drink.

The woman watched Ben. He was a stranger. She would know. She knew everybody in the tiny town. Strangers were cause for curiosity, and as she studied his back she wondered just who he was. It was far too early in the year for tourists.

Stranger. She guessed that she'd heard the word a thousand times

102

to describe visitors. Anyone who hadn't been born in Grand Marais, or had not lived there for more than five years was known as a stranger. And yet it was she who felt like a stranger, though she had been born and raised in Grand Marais. Years ago, she dreamed that one day she would leave the area. She might even go as far as California. The land of fruits and nuts. That's what people in Grand Marais called California. But that was okay with her. Maybe there she'd fit in, find a niche. Maybe out there she'd find a man, a good man. Oh, she'd found a man in Grand Marais, all right, but he hadn't been a good man. What a lousy marriage she'd had with him. Then after two years he took off. He got to California instead of her! Or maybe it was Oregon. She wasn't real sure. What she did know was that she didn't date local men now. She simply got on with her life, worked in the restaurant and tried to stay busy with little hobbies like sewing and building a collection of dried wild flowers. She also waited, sure that one day a handsome stranger would visit Grand Marais and cast an eye in her direction.

"Hi there," a voice from behind said cheerfully.

Ben turned his head to find the woman standing beside him . "Oh, hi," he said, feeling somewhat clumsy.

"Mind if I join you?"

"No, sure, have a seat," he stammered.

She slid onto a bar stool and said, "Don't be shocked. Us girls in the U.P. are aggressive."

He smiled and nodded, not quite sure how to reply.

"We have to be aggressive," the woman continued, "there are hardly any eligible men around these parts so when we see someone we like we go for it." She smiled broadly.

He looked into her eyes and thought they were the bluest, most beautiful eyes he'd ever seen. "My name's Ben, Ben Adams."

"Nice to meet you Ben, Ben Adams." She laughed out loud at the joke. "My name is Mars." She stuck out her hand to shake.

"Mars?" Ben asked, cocking his head to one side as though he'd heard incorrectly.

"Yeah, like the little, red planet."

"Funny, you don't look like a little green creature from Mars."

"No, but my mother got the idea for the name when she was in the hospital having me. Apparently she was in labor for some ungodly number of hours. While she was lying there suffering she tried to take her mind off the pain by staring out the window at this bright light in the sky. She said that light stayed in the sky all night long. Just before they wheeled her

103

away to have me she asked the nurse what the light was. The nurse said she thought it was the planet Mars. And, voila, here I am!" She performed a mock bow and giggled.

"Would you like a drink, Mars?"

"I'd love one, but I'm working all the way to closing so I can't, but until somebody orders some food I can sit here and talk."

"That would be nice," he said sincerely.

"Let's dance," Mars said suddenly, jumping off the bar stool and grabbing him by the arm.

"But I don't dance," he replied, pulling back. "If there's one thing I don't do, it's dance."

"No buts about it, everybody in the U.P. dances. I guess that's how we stay warm up here. Come on." She tugged his arm and literally dragged him off the bar stool.

He reluctantly followed her to the dance area and they joined the other couples. He shifted his feet self consciously, not quite sure how to do the polka/jitter bug. When the song ended Mars insisted they continue dancing. Ben shot a loving look at his drink on the bar, but decided that he liked dancing with this pretty woman. By the end of the next song he was actually getting into the swing of things and by then it was one of those times where everyone is laughing and having a good time. During a break in the music Mars introduced him around to the others and they all shook hands and grinned at one another.

They finally took a break, collapsing onto their bar stools. Ben grabbed a paper napkin and wiped his brow. Mars' cheeks were flushed a bright red. She ordered a Coke and drank it down in one long gulp. Then she fixed her eyes on Ben. She liked the way he looked. She didn't think that he was particularly handsome, but he had an appeal. She thought it might be his swarthy complexion and the deep lines that creased his face, making him look much older than she guessed he really was. There was something else about him, some thread, she sensed that was pulling her inexorably forward. She studied his profile for a moment until he turned and looked at her. And there it was! His eyes. She saw the same sadness, the same loneliness, the same lack of hope she saw in her own eyes when she studied herself in the mirror. She had managed to push those feelings away, to wrap them up and stick them in a dark closet in the back of her mind. As she watched Ben she felt a sharp pop, a twinge, a stirring beneath her skin that gradually coursed through her entire body. The feeling was so real she almost gasped. She felt the hair on her head prickle, and suddenly the scene in the bar diminished, lost all its focus, until all she saw

104

was Ben. Now as she looked at him she wanted more than anything to throw her arms around his neck, to feel the warmth of their skin against one another.

"So what brings you to Grand Marais, Ben?" she asked, trying to sound chipper.

His mood abruptly changed and he looked away.

"Did I say something wrong?"

"No, I'm sorry," he said. "I'm up here to get away from things. I...I've...got something to do up here."

Mars continued to study him. "You've got a funny accent. Where are you from?"

"I'm from the south originally, but I've been living just on the other side of the bridge for the last few years."

"Down state!" Mars shrieked in mock horror. "Oh, no, I'm sitting with a down stater!" She turned to the others in the bar and shouted, "I've been dancing with a troll!"

"A troll?" Ben asked. He gave her a bewildered look.

"Oh don't feel bad, that's what all down staters are called."

Ben shook his head back and forth. "I still don't understand."

"You live down state, below the Mackinac bridge. Get it? Everyone who lives below the bridge is a troll." She laughed easily.

"That makes me a troll all right," Ben said, and then joining the fun he turned to the others and yelled, "I'm a troll!"

"Give the troll another drink on me," Willy shouted from his end of the bar. Everyone laughed and it was like one big, happy party.

Suddenly, Mars leaned forward and planted a quick kiss on Ben's lips.

"What was that for?" Ben asked, surprised.

"Didn't you like it?"

He thought for a moment and replied, "I loved it!"

"I wanted to see if I'd turn into a troll if I kissed one."

"It's probably the other way around."

What do you mean?"

"Maybe your kiss will turn me from a troll into a prince or something." He hesitated for a moment, his eyes fixed earnestly on her. "I think you're the most beautiful person I've ever met."

"And you've been drinking too much." A fat woman stuck her head through the shutter doors and waved at Mars. "Oops, gotta go. Don't go away, I'll be back a little later."

Ben got himself into a spirited game of darts and before long it seemed to him that he'd been coming into this bar all his life. Towards dinner time more of a crowd filtered through the door and many of the people ordered food. Mars was gone for over two hours and by the time she managed to return Ben was drunk and sitting at a table with a group of men.

"I can see that you're in trouble now," she teased Ben, as she surveyed the group of men at the table. "Did you miss me?"

"I did," he answered honestly, looking at her intently.

Someone played a slow tune on the juke box and Ben asked Mars to dance. More couples joined them in the small dance area. Ben felt himself pushed closer to Mars. He could smell her perfume mixed with the spicy odors of the kitchen. Her cheek felt warm against his. He held her tightly as they swayed to the gentle dance music, and he thought, for a moment, that he could feel his heart beating in his chest.

"She's a nice girl, that Mars," one of the men said when Ben rejoined the group. "She won't have anything to do with any of us rough necks, but she likes you."

"Yes, she does," another man added.

Much later, Ben ended up sitting alone at a table with Mars. The kitchen was closed and she had finished cleaning up. Every now and then she had to clear a table or deliver some drinks, but many of the customers had left so she was able to spend a lot of time talking with Ben. During the course of the evening Ben's thoughts had constantly returned to his mission in Grand Marais. Even as he sat at the crowded table listening to the other men's jokes and stories he had found himself debating whether or not to put the revolver in his mouth or to his temple. Now, as he sat quietly talking and laughing with Mars, those thoughts seemed to be a part of another person, who was living another life. Mars had a habit of touching his hand every now and then as she spoke. Each time her he felt her touch, Ben would watch her hand longingly as if this touch were some sort of connection, as if it were a tether to the human race.

They talked until it became closing time. The bartender blinked the lights several times. Willy was the only one at the bar and he left without an argument, staggering clumsily to the door.

"Sorry, Mars, but you and your friend have to go, too," the bartender said as he approached their table.

Ben didn't want to go. He didn't want this evening to end. The bartender had referred to him as Mars' friend, and Ben liked that. He'd only met this woman a few hours earlier and yet he did think of her as his friend. He liked the feeling.

Outside they could see their breath in the air. "It's supposed to be a pretty day tomorrow," Mars said. "Oh, look at the stars!"

Ben looked up and my God the stars were so bright they looked as if he could reach up and touch them.

"Let's go on a picnic tomorrow afternoon," Mars said. "It's supposed to warm up into the sixties. It will be a nice day. I'll take you to a special place." She looked into Ben's eyes with a sincerity so powerful that it moved him.

"All right," he said, smiling shyly.

"Then it's settled. Meet me right here at two. I'll bring everything." She stepped to her tiptoes and kissed him gently on the cheek. Then she hurried away, disappearing into the dark.

It was nearly one in the afternoon when he woke up. The dew and scattered frost had burned off and it was a glorious day. The sun was warm and there wasn't a cloud in the sky. He showered and dressed before taking a stroll along the beach on his way toward the bar. And what a fabulous day it was! The air was brisk and clear and filled with that wonderful clean smell that only comes when you're near a large body of water and the wind is blowing in. When he reached the bar Mars was waiting out front, standing in the dappled sunlight beneath the new leaves of a large birch tree. She carried a wicker picnic hamper. The necks of two wine bottles protruded from the basket.

"I hope that you had a good time last night," she said, kissing him lightly on the cheek. "I think that sometimes I forget to appreciate what a nice little town this is. Last night reminded me."

Ben said, "I had a great time." He kissed her back on the cheek. "It's good to see you."

"And, it's good to see you, too. Ready to go to the dunes?"

"Yeah, and believe it or not, I'm hungry as a bear."

"Good, I've got fried white fish, hot sauce, German potato salad and ice cold white wine. Come on, we'll take my car."

They drove out to Sable Dunes and hiked through a stand of trees to a place out of the wind where they had a magnificent view of Lake Superior. Mars spread a giant, green tartan blanket on the sand and they sat down. Ben found the cork screw and nervously wrestled with one of the bottles, but then he looked at Mars. She smiled, holding his gaze, and all at once they were locked in a fumbling embrace, frantically kissing and pressing against each other. They fell back, entwined, on the blanket. They kissed and held each other for a long time. Ben felt himself slip into that dreamlike state of sensuous passion that only comes from being with a person you love a great deal. And then all at once he remembered why he had come to Grand Marais. There was an ache, not mental, but physical, that caused his entire body to shudder as he remembered his desire to kill himself. He suddenly felt as if some invisible hand had grabbed him, slapped his face, yanking him back to reality. He pulled away from her arms and stood up, staring morosely out at the blue lake and to the dark hills in the distance. He squinted his eyes in the late afternoon sunlight, still bright, but no longer warm on his face. He thought the air held the fragrance of wild grapes, but, of course, it was far too early in the season for that. And then he realized that it must be her perfume or bath cologne or maybe only the natural scent of her skin, fresh and clean.

She asked, "What's wrong?"

"I've got a lot of problems," he began. "I came to Grand Marais...," he hesitated, "I don't know, I'm so mixed up..."

Mars interrupted, "It doesn't matter. Nothing matters. We're together now." She stood up and faced him. "Look at me."

He turned and looked at her with a yearning he hadn't felt for a very long time. She was gorgeous and he stared deeply into her eyes. He pulled her into his arms and they sank down on the dark blanket, still slightly warm from the sun. The air was cool and the wind had quartered and blew along the slope of the dunes, swirling sand in the air.

Ben kissed her gently and then passionately. They huddled against the wind in each others arms for a long time. Finally Mars sat up and looked him directly in the eyes.

"I know you must have been very unhappy. I don't have ESP or anything, but almost any woman could see this in you. You need to put all that in the past."

"How do you do that?" He cocked his head to one side and looked at her. "How can I ever forget why it is that I came up here?"

"I can take care of you and you can take care of me. I've been unhappy, too. We can lean on each other and love each other and make each other happy."

"That would be nice, but..."

"No buts about it, remember. I know you had another life, a troll's life down state, but you can just leave it and disappear up here. Yes," she said, thinking about it, "you can just disappear up here in the U.P. and start all over with me. Ben, stay and move in with me. Please, Ben, disappear in the U.P. and stay with me." She held out her hands and he gratefully fell into her arms. He leaned his head on her shoulder and quietly wept.

There was a fleeting moment of release as he felt himself separate

108

from all that he'd known and endured. A stern breeze rushed through the dune grass with a whistle, sounding, Ben thought, like the whispers of a thousand angels. Mars held him tightly and stroked the back of his head, rocking him ever so gently.

After a while it became much too cold for the dunes so they shook the sand from the blanket and carefully folded it into a square. "Come on, we'll eat our food at home," Mars said, leading him back to the car.

They reached the car and she drove to town, slowly following the two track through the darkening, heavy woods. Ben leaned back against his head rest. He closed his eyes and took a deep, cleansing breath, smiling as he savored the simple beauty of life.

ONCE A MAN, TWICE A CHILD

While Orlando Smith, or Mr. Jum as most people called him, was confined to the state run hospital he had a vision. The vision was more like a fond memory, a leftover, from what Mr. Jum called the olden days. In his vision he saw the boy, only now the boy was his very own son.

He smiled contentedly at this thought. The boy had meant everything to him, but that was so very long ago. For the last several months he had been losing his memory. Sometimes, he would sit in his cracked and brittle vinyl chair trying for the life of him to remember some detail from the past. He spent an entire afternoon once, puffing on his pipe, his bald head encircled in a nimbus of white, sweet smelling smoke, trying to recall the name of the Jones boy, the one from down the street who had spent so much time at the house. But everything was just a blur, a happy blob of events that, when considered as a whole, often caused him to chuckle. He could close his eyes and catch flakes or chips, golden they seemed to him, yes, golden snatches of long ago memories, when the boy had been his son.

Mr. Jum looked down at his tired black hands, resting awkwardly in his lap. The hands were dry, as cracked and brittle as the old chair in which he was sitting. So dry that they were lined with a patchwork of deep, grey white creases. Those hands had always been busy. They weren't used to resting for long periods of time. But that was a long time ago, too.

How old was he, he wondered? Years ago for the Social Security records he picked an age out of the air. If he continued to play by those rules he'd be eighty two years old now. Secretly, he thought he was probably a good five or six years older. His parents had been born slaves in Kentucky. After the war they moved with a pocket of timid, newly freed blacks to the rural town of Paris, Missouri. Paris had been there for years, but after the war it took shape as a community, a black community. Mr. Jum was born into a time and place where the war and the feelings of southern whites were muted. Scratching out a meager living on a piece of rocky sod was the same hardship for everyone in Paris. Color gave way to just staying alive. But there was class distinction. The whites held to that belief, though somewhat sluggishly, and not much emphasis was put on it. People in Paris were too tired, too consumed with making it through the throbbing summer heat, making sure there was enough firewood to last the winter, staying one step ahead of the bill collector. As long as everybody kept their place, Paris was a good place to live.

The boy was already ten years old when Mr. Jum and his wife, Nita, answered an ad in the St. Louis Sunday paper. Mr. Jum couldn't read or write and Nita didn't quite understand what "domestic help" meant, but the thought of doing yard work and cooking meals for a rich, white family sounded appealing. Following the Second World War money in Paris all but disappeared. By this time Mr. Jum had already lived a lifetime. He had farmed and worked an assortment of menial jobs. At his age there simply were no more opportunities left in Paris. Moving to St. Louis had become a necessity, though at the time it took on the cachet of an around the world cruise. And Nita and Mr. Jum might as well have been taking off for the far flung corners of the world, such was their view of moving to the big city.

The Baileys had two children: The wild, incorrigible boy, Sammy, and his quiet, somewhat sad faced older sister, Dee Dee. Sammy fell in love with Nita and Mr. Jum immediately, while Dee Dee cried and demanded to know why her parents insisted on having strangers move into the house. Mrs. Bailey held the same apprehension, but her need for "live in help" was strong enough to overcome these pangs and her daughter's whining. Mrs. Bailey had problems with moodiness. She could be the loving mother, at once concerned with the well being of everyone in the family. But then for some inexplicable reason, perhaps an unintentional slight, an oppressive summer day, the stress of an upcoming holiday and she would silently stumble into days of depression and take to her bed. Most days, the thought of facing housework or cooking a meal overwhelmed her. She had been reared in a gracious lifestyle and never quite understood or tolerated the basic elements of being a housewife. Mr. Bailey had hopes that live in servants would ease his wife's frustration.

Sammy remembered that first, uneventful meeting, when they all gathered in the formal living room to meet Nita and Mr. Jum as a day burnished with age. He has the distinct memory of being a young child in an old setting. The house was like a museum. It had been built at the turn of the century at a time when there were no worries about heating bills or maintenance. The house was endlessly fascinating to him with cavernous room after room, high ceilings, hidden closets and shelves, front and back stairs, a third floor servant's quarters. And his parents fit quite well into the house. They were both in their fifties and enjoyed the space that was usually so elusive to families with young children. The children had appeared as though an afterthought. Mrs. Bailey hadn't been able to have children. After many years, enough years that most couples would have forgotten about having a family, they discussed adoption. Maybe this would finally make her happy, Mr. Bailey had thought at the time. Just let me adopt a pretty, little girl, Mrs. Bailey had begged. A little girl who I can dress up and take to mass on Sunday mornings. At last, a deal was struck. Mr. Bailey would allow her to adopt a little girl, but only if within a few years they adopted another child. He had seen far too many spoiled children, the result of a single child family.

And so there were Dee Dee and Sammy, as different as night and day. He had dark brown hair and a swarthy middle European complexion while she was a blond with deep blue eyes. He loved to laugh and play with other kids, while she scowled and was suspicious of others. He was deep chested and had a long, thin face. He was robust, if not overly energetic. Her wan, oval face framed a pouting mouth that later in life some men would think sensuous. Her eyes held the tired look of an old person. The children may have been nothing alike, but even before the day they were called into the living room and told that they were adopted they sensed that they were tied together by a bond stronger than any family's blood. They were devoted to each other, possibly because they knew there were no other relatives in the family. Even at this early age both children grasped the inevitable truth that sooner or later all they would have would be each other. And yet, like most siblings they fought bitterly at times. "You love your sister, don't you?" his mother would ask. He'd nod his head diligently, knowing that this was the correct response. "And, you love your brother, don't you?" "No, I hate him! He's awful! How can you stand Sammy the brat?"

But they were close. One time Sammy found a baby robin squawking raucously in the mottled shade of the large oak trees that framed the back yard. The bird could not have been more than a day old

112

and somehow had fallen from it's nest. Sammy took the bird inside the house and built a small nest in a shoe box. He tried to force warm milk into the tiny beak with an eye dropper. The bird only held it's head in the air and cried pitifully. That evening Sammy went downstairs to dinner. He gobbled down his food, anxious to return to his bird. During the meal he excitedly told the rest of the family about the baby robin. He couldn't quite make the others understand that the baby bird had suddenly become something very special to him. This was his pet, his new best friend. After dinner Sammy ran back to his room. He peered into the shoe box expectantly, and looked at the baby robin. The bird was dead, it's nearly bald body dull and limp. Sammy was beside himself with grief.

That night in bed he tried not to make any sound as he cried. Dee Dee came into his room looking for something. She timidly looked into the shoe box and surveyed the dead bird. Her first instinct was to cover her mouth and run from the room. Instead, she calmly sat down on the edge of the bed and held her brother's hand. After a while, she stood up and carried the shoe box outside to the far reaches of the back yard, to a place overgrown with dense lilac bushes and swarming vines. Sammy silently followed her, barefoot and in his pajamas. He shivered slightly in the damp, cool air. The overwhelming aroma of the lilac bushes seemed to envelope and smother him. Using sticks they carefully cleared a spot of earth and dug a shallow grave. Dee Dee dumped the bird into the hole and quickly filled the grave, smoothing the little plot with her hand. "Your bird is happy now," she said, smiling at Sammy. Then she led him back into the dark house.

Oddly enough, Mrs. Bailey found herself pulled to the little boy, who she said reminded her of a miniature Maurice Chevalier, an actor quite popular with the women at the time. Dee Dee gravitated toward her father, and she learned at an early age how to manipulate him. She would sit on his lap and smile into his broad face. He indulged her with her every whim. Whenever she wanted something or had a problem she ran directly to her father.

The elderly parents, sat stiffly in their wing chairs, the children forced to sit quietly on the couch waiting for Nita and Mr. Jum to arrive. No one talked. The father had removed his tie and undone the top two buttons of his shirt in an effort to beat the heat. His shirt sleeves were rolled up past the elbows. His face was flushed and he perspired heavily. He held a gin and tonic that dripped condensation on his chest whenever he tilted the glass to his lips. Mr. Bailey was a successful insurance executive. He had made many friends in business and he was highly

113

regarded in the community. Many people sought his advice, both in business and personal matters, because they thought he possessed an uncanny common sense. He seemingly always knew what was the right thing to do. His wife on the other hand preferred to float through life. Any bump in the road upset her. She thought she was doing extremely well just to make it from one day to the next. This particular afternoon she sat in her favorite chair looking cool and relaxed, almost airy as if she'd blown in on the gentle wind that occasionally billowed the window curtains. The boy fidgeted while his sister sulked, surveying the world through narrowed, observant eyes, as though she were highly suspicious of the entire matter. The living room was silent, overlaid by the sound of the large, banjo wall clock ticking with every pendulum swing. It was early summer and already the Missouri heat hung like a blanket in the air.

And then here they were, Nita and Mr. Jum, the new additions to the family. My Lord, but they were old! Mr. Jum wore a dark, loose fitting suit, shiny with age. He was a small man, perhaps only five foot six, with a bald head, but his eyes twinkled in such a way that Sammy was immediately drawn to him. His jet black skin was as shiny as his worn Sunday suit. His head glistened with a film of perspiration and after he sat down he pulled an oversize, white handkerchief from his back pant's pocket and rubbed his head as if he were polishing a bowling ball. He had square shoulders and thick muscles. Even at his age it was easy to see that he was a powerful man capable of hard work and heavy lifting. The veins on his hands popped out forming dark rivers that disappeared into his shirt sleeves.

Nita was a tiny, fat woman. She had a perfectly round face with crow's feet wrinkles at the corners of her eyes. Her short, glossy hair was pulled back severely to a small bun that was held in place by a dozen bobby pins. She wore a light grey uniform with short sleeves that revealed black, doughy arms. When she sat in her chair her feet didn't reach the floor, and she sat there smiling as if this was the happiest day of her life.

The introductions were brief. Mr. Bailey outlined the rules: Every Thursday was their day off, as was every other Sunday. First thing each morning Mr. Jum was to wash the cars. Two rings from the bedroom buzzer that rang in the kitchen meant Nita was to start Mr. Bailey's breakfast, three rings called for Mrs. Bailey's breakfast. They never ate breakfast together. He was up and off to the office, while she lazed about in bed usually until ten or ten thirty. There were a litany of other rules, and the old, black couple listened attentively, nodding their heads whenever Mr. Bailey looked at them. And so here they sat, two children surrounded

114

by age. The parents in their mid fifties, who through the years had attained a financial and social level to be admired, two very old, black people from the country and the old house, ticking and creaking and sighing, filled with the mustiness of old wood, the coolness of dark rooms, the lingering gayety of bygone parties, and in the summer when the windows were open to catch the breeze, the house filled with the cloying fragrance of the honeysuckle bushes that bordered the long driveway.

"Now, is your name really Jum?" Mrs. Bailey was asking.

"It's Orlando, ma'am," he answered in a voice no louder than a whisper.

"People call him Jum, though," Nita added quickly. She dropped her head shyly and stared at her lap.

"I have a hard time with Jum," Mrs. Bailey said. "It sounds too country for me. Why don't we call you John. Is that OK with you?" She smiled with a sense of finality, glad that that bit of unpleasantness was out of the way.

"Are you really from Paris?" Sammy asked enthusiastically.

Dee Dee asked tiredly, "May I go now?" She slid from her chair, and without waiting for an answer, huffed out of the room.

"Yes," Mr. Jum answered.

"Paris? Really?"

"Yes, we're from Paris."

"Let me hear you speak some French then."

Everyone laughed lightly. "They're from a little town called Paris in central Missouri," Mrs. Bailey said. She smiled tenderly at her son.

By that afternoon Sammy was leading a contingent of neighborhood children to the third floor quarters where Nita and Mr. Jum were busily moving in. The old couple had lugged a dozen or more water stained corrugated boxes up the narrow, winding stairs. An assortment of mismatched, battered luggage stood in the middle of the floor. Their quarters consisted of a sitting room, a bedroom and a bathroom. A radio with cracked plastic housing sat on the table softly emitting black gospel music. The children stood gathered in the sitting room doorway watching as the boxes were carefully unpacked. Sammy had already taught Mr. Jum to say, "Oui, oui, Monsieur."

"Mr. Jum is from Paris. Isn't that right, Mr. Jum?" Sammy said for the other kid's benefit.

"Oui, oui, Monsieur," the old man said in his husky voice. The children squealed with delight, and Mr. Jum beamed from ear to ear as happy as any of the kids.

Sammy stayed on long after the other children had gone home for dinner. He liked being with Nita and Mr. Jum. As the couple continued with their unpacking he peppered Mr. Jum with questions.

"Do you know how to wrestle?"

"I was the best wrestler in Paris," Mr. Jum bragged. "Men came from all over the county to try and throw me. I had a special move where I'd grab 'em by the legs and pitch 'em over my hip."

"Teach me that move, Mr. Jum!"

"Maybe tomorrow. Right now, I've got to get these here belongings put up or Miss Nita will be hollerin' after me."

When Sammy returned to the third floor following his dinner he saw that the unpacking was nearly complete. The empty boxes were stacked and lined against one wall, where as far as he could remember they stayed for nearly eleven years. A single table lamp cast a hazy circle of light in one corner of the room. Mr. Jum was sitting in a tattered easy chair, his unlit pipe in his mouth, listening to the radio. Nita sat at the table sorting buttons from a cigar box. A large fan was perched backwards in the open window sucking air from the stuffy room. Sammy stood quietly in the doorway.

"Come on in and sit a spell," Mr. Jum said without looking at the boy.

Sammy edged into the room. "How'd you know I was here?" he asked.

"Indians taught me how to listen for footsteps."

"Indians?"

"And I got me a special eye, too. I can see out the back of my head."

"Go on," Sammy said, but he was amazed and crept closer.

Nita smiled to herself, not bothering to look up from her work.

"Come on over here and I'll show you."

Sammy sat cross legged on the floor with his elbows on his knees, holding his head in his hands, staring up at Mr. Jum.

Mr. Jum took off his glasses and put both hands over one eye. When he pulled his hands away the eyelid had been turned inside out so that only the white part of his eye could be seen. Sammy stared, open mouthed, at the eye.

At last he said, "Wow! Teach me how to do that."

"Maybe tomorrow. Right now we have to be quiet 'cause our show is coming on the radio."

"What show?" Sammy asked.

116

"Grand 'Ol Opry, sweetie," Nita answered. "It's Mr. Jum's favorite."

"Can I stay and listen?"

Mr. Jum said, "Sure."

But just then Sammy's mother called up the stairs that it was time to get ready for bed. "Okay, in a minute," he responded.

A half hour later she called again. This time he reluctantly went downstairs. When he was ready for bed he found his parents in the living room watching television. He crawled onto his mother's lap. He was big enough that his weight bothered her, but this had been their nightly ritual since he was a baby. He put his head on her shoulder and stared absentmindedly at the flickering television screen. His mother began to stroke his forehead, brushing his dark bangs back and rubbing her fingertips just over his eyebrows.

"I like Nita and Mr. Jum," he said.

"It's Nita and John," his mother corrected.

"His name is Mr. Jum," he replied indignantly.

"You can call him Jum, honey."

"Can I sleep with you tonight?"

"You've got your own bedroom and your own bed," she said softly.

"But I get scared."

His father cut in. "Sammy, you're too old to sleep with us. Now there's nothing to be scared of and you know it."

"Can I stay down here until I fall asleep?"

"Okay," his father replied, "but this has got to stop, too. You're getting too heavy for me to carry up those stairs. Besides, you're too old to be frightened of the dark. After all, aren't you the same Sammy Bailey who scored the most touchdowns on the fifth grade Peewee football team?"

The boy started to object, but then stared in silence at his father. It was true. He was an extraordinary athlete, and big for his age. Already the childhood chubbiness was yielding to stringy muscle, and within the year his voice would turn croaky.

He closed his eyes, enjoying the security of being in his mother's arms. He concentrated on her stroking his forehead, smiling, until he fell asleep.

When he was sound asleep his father carried him to his bedroom and put him to bed. Dee Dee was in her room talking on the phone she'd received for her last birthday. She was complaining about Nita and Mr. Jum.

"It's just awful having these black people in our house," she was saying. "Of course, Sammy the brat thinks they're just great. Wouldn't you know it!"

She was speaking to her boyfriend of the week. She had already decided that she would have nothing to do with Nita and Mr. Jum.

Later in the night Sammy woke up, certain that he had heard some strange noise. He sat up in his bed and looked about the dark room. A faint shaft of moonlight fell through the open window forming a gauzy puddle on the floor. The boy watched as a figure carrying a large white sack walked aimlessly about the room. The apparition stopped, gazed for a moment at him and then disappeared. Sammy hightailed it for his parent's bedroom.

He cautiously, and as silently as possible, pushed open the door to their room. He could hear his father snoring. Sammy crept to the foot of their bed. He slowly tugged the summer comforter from the foot of the bed and made a little nest for himself on the floor.

He hadn't been settled for more than a minute when his mother said in a loud, clear voice, "Sammy, what are you doing in here?"

His father grumbled sleepily, "Oh, for God's sake!"

"There was someone in my room," Sammy whimpered.

"There's no one in your room," his mother said emphatically.

"I saw him. It was a ghost."

"There's no ghost in your room," his father said angrily. "Now you get back to your bed right now."

"But, Dad---"

"If I have to get out of this bed there's going to be trouble," his father warned.

Sammy reluctantly left the room, complaining under his breath that his parents didn't care about the trouble that lurked in his room. Now, he decided to investigate Nita and Mr. Jum's bedroom. He climbed the narrow stairs to the third floor. The fan still hummed in the sitting room window. From the open bedroom door he could hear the rhythmic breathing of the old people. He dropped to his hands and knees and crawled into the room. When he reached the double bed he reached up feeling along the pillow. His hand touched Mr. Jum's bald head and the old man stirred.

"Who's there?" Mr. Jum said softly.

Sammy jerked his hand away and remained quiet.

"Is that you, Sammy?"

Sammy whispered, "Yes, Mr. Jum, it's me."

"What you doin' here in the middle of the night, boy?"

"I'm scared."

"Scared of what?"

Nita was awake now and sat up in bed.

"I saw something in my room. I think it was a ghost."

"You need a night light in your room. That will scare off them ghosts," Mr. Jum announced.

"I don't have a night light."

"Then we'll have to make one for you. Come on," Mr. Jum said, climbing out of bed. He put on his bathrobe and slippers and then led the boy down to the kitchen. "Where would I find an empty glass jar?"

Sammy went to one of the pantry cupboards and rummaged around in the dark. At last he produced a Mason jar with a screw on lid and handed it to Mr. Jum.

"You sit here at the window while I go outside and get your night light made," Mr. Jum said.

The boy pulled a chair over to one of the windows and sat down. In a moment Mr. Jum appeared in the backyard. Sammy watched in fascination as the old man scampered after the tiny fireflies that intermittently lit the darkness. He loped through the yard looking like a parody of a ballet dancer. Every few seconds he caught a firefly and hurriedly thrust it into the Mason jar. Soon the jar held enough bugs that it looked like some flashing neon light that had been caught in a bottle.

Upon returning to the kitchen Mr. Jum held up the jar and said, "Here's your night light, boy."

"Gosh!" was all Sammy could say.

"After I punch some holes in the lid you'll be all set to get some sleep."

"That will keep the ghosts away, Mr. Jum?"

"That's for sure."

That night, and every night for the rest of the summer Sammy fell asleep to the phosphorescent twinkling of dozens of bottled fireflies. It became a nightly ritual, the old black man tripping through the yard catching fireflies so that his young friend wouldn't be afraid of the dark.

When Sammy awoke the next morning, Sunday, he could hear his sister complaining about the bacon Nita had prepared for breakfast. Her braying, singsong voice rushed up the back stairwell.

"This bacon is too crisp! Where did you learn to cook? Oh, never mind, I won't eat breakfast. I've got to get ready for church."

After church Sammy found Mr. Jum on the third floor putting a new lock on the landing door.

"Why are you putting a new lock on the door?" Sammy asked as he watched Mr. Jum tighten a set of shiny brass screws.

"We've got to have some privacy for our rooms."

"Why?"

"Because we don't want no mess of kids going through our rooms while we're downstairs working."

"I wouldn't go in your rooms when you're not there," Sammy insisted.

"Here, let me show you a trick," Mr. Jum said, smiling.

Sammy noticed that his teeth were perfectly shaped and very white, and he wondered if they were false teeth. He made a mental note to find out.

"I'm going to put a piece of tape over the lock to keep the door from locking," Mr. Jum continued. He carefully stretched a short piece of white bandage tape over the cylinder part of the lock that fits into the metal plate. "That will keep the door from locking until I can get downtown this Thursday and get an extra key made."

"Wow!" Sammy whistled under his breath.

That evening he secretly placed a piece of tape over the lock on the door to the bathroom that he shared with his sister. Then he scoured the neighborhood lining up customers, who were willing to pay him a nickel. The gang of boys hid out by the garage watching for lights in the bathroom window. The boys waited breathlessly as the early summer dusk settled through the uppermost branches of the large oak tree that shaded the house. Suddenly, the harsh glare of the bathroom light lit the window, signaling Sammy that it was show time. He led the giggling band up the back stairs where they assembled in a jostling group by the rigged door. Sammy listened until he heard Dee Dee splashing in the tub. Then banging the door wide open, and whooping like wild Indians, the boys crowded into the bathroom. There was nothing to see, Dee Dee being totally submerged in a frothy mass of bubbles, but still, her mouth fell open and she stared in disbelief at the group of wide eyed boys. She quickly recovered and let out the most piercing scream Sammy had ever heard. She kept screaming hysterically, her high pitched wail filling the entire house. She thrashed about helplessly in the tub throwing suds wildly into the air. The boys took off down the back stairs and hid in a clump of bushes behind the garage.

That night Sammy was sent to bed without any dinner and told that he had lost his television privileges for one week. He sulked about his dark room wishing that he had a candy bar or some popcorn. When it was late and he could tell that the rest of the family had gone to bed he considered sneaking down to the kitchen for some food. But, he knew that if he was caught it only meant a more severe punishment, possibly even a few smacks across the rear end with his father's leather belt. He was hungry, but knew better than to risk a spanking.

He was on his stomach on top of the bed covers when he heard the door to his room creak open. He looked around, thinking that maybe his father had decided on a spanking after all, but instead there stood Mr. Jum, holding a jar of fireflies in one hand and a plate of fried chicken in the other.

It took another two years before Dee Dee would grudgingly accept Nita and Mr. Jum. She still didn't care for them, but had realized that there were definite benefits to having them around. She always had fresh laundry and ironed blouses, her normally messy room was immaculate every day when she arrived home from school and there was always a batch of just baked chocolate chip cookies in the kitchen. Nita loved to make chocolate chip cookies and Dee Dee loved to eat them. She devoured the cookies with such passion that Nita finally was forced to hide plates of the cookies about the kitchen so there would be some left for the rest of the family. Mrs. Bailey liked the way Nita took total control of the kitchen. It meant that there was just that much more time for her to be, well... a woman of leisure, and this had become quite important to her. The extent of her involvement in the kitchen was to plan the weekly dinner menus, but even this chore took on an air of family fun. It soon became a Sunday night ritual for the parents and two kids to gather in the living room to select the menu. Sammy was one of those kids who like practically everything put before them on a plate so he gleefully joined in on the planning. Dee Dee thought the entire process was a waste of time.

By this time Nita and Mr. Jum were fully trusted. The Baileys felt comfortable with leaving town for a what Mrs. Bailey took to calling their second honeymoon. Dee Dee was extremely insulted over being left, especially in the care of Nita and Mr. Jum. Now, her complaint was that she was too old to have what appeared to be baby sitters. But it didn't take her long to figure out that with a bit of strategic planning she would be able to out fox the elderly couple. Why, she'd be able to stay out way past her curfew. She might even have a party, invite a bunch of kids over to listen to music. In the end she smiled coyly as her parents climbed into the airport taxi.

Sammy's joy was immense. When his parents drove off he tried to contain himself, but inside he trembled with anticipation. His parent's vacation meant extra time with his pal, Mr. Jum, who had filled his head with plans for a log fort in the back yard, games of hide and seek and cooking fish on an open fire that he'd build out by the driveway. Mr. Jum was happy, too. He loved the boy, and when Sammy sat at his feet listening to the Grand 'Ol Opry on the radio Mr. Jum didn't see a white boy. He didn't see a little black child either. What he saw was a person whom he loved with all his might. Every night Mr. Jum felt a pinch of sadness in his throat when he had to say good night to Sammy.

The first night his parents were gone Sammy was apprehensive about sleeping by himself. That may sound strange for a boy nearly thirteen years old, but he was a sensitive child, a bit insecure, and the huge house with room after dark room spilling out from each other terrified him when the lights were out. The house was full of night sounds, too. Creaking and moaning as it settled. Every sound was a threat to Sammy, a burglar trying to pry open a window, a motorcycle gang that had lost its way, maybe even Dracula, who had suddenly materialized from the Bela Lugosi movie he'd watched a few nights earlier. Mr. Jum tucked him into his bed, but it was winter and there were no fireflies. Sometime during the darkest part of the night Sammy woke up screaming. He couldn't remember if it was a nightmare or he had actually heard a windowpane shatter. Within a minute Mr. Jum was standing in his room. He sat down on the edge of the bed and Sammy told him about the sound.

"You go back to sleep now, boy," Mr. Jum whispered. "I'll stay right here."

"I'm afraid, Mr. Jum," Sammy pleaded.

"Don't be afraid, I'm here."

Mr. Jum sat on the bed for a long time. Finally, he curled himself into a ball at the foot of the bed and went to sleep. He was still there when Sammy woke up in the morning.

The following Saturday Mr. Jum made good on his promise to build a fort. He used fireplace logs. Meticulously, he worked stacking and nailing until he had produced a miniature log cabin. It was big enough for three or four kids. Sammy had some friends over and the group, fortified with a huge bowl of popcorn that Nita had popped, played in the fort for most of the afternoon. Then they held relay races in the driveway. Mr. Jum may have been an old man, but he sure could run fast. He beat the young teenagers every time.

When the other children had left Mr. Jum showed Sammy how if he put his ear to the second floor laundry chute he could listen to his sister as she talked on the phone in the basement. She called it the rathskeller. She had talked her father into putting a carpet, a couch and two chairs, a telephone and a television set in one corner. This was her space, and strictly off limits to Sammy. As a result the rathskeller always held a certain fascination for Sammy. The idea of being able to listen in on all her conversations thrilled him to no end.

That night Dee Dee went out on a date with her latest steady boyfriend, Buddy Harrison. The light was fading when Nita, Mr. Jum and Sammy cooked catfish over an open fire built in the driveway. Mr. Jum loved fresh catfish, but after the first time he cooked some for himself Mrs. Bailey said no more fish cooking in the kitchen. She claimed that her bedroom smelled like a cheap seafood restaurant that had forgotten to change the frying oil. No matter, the three of them sat Indian style on the ground and watched the catfish and potatoes sputter in the hot oil. Mr. Jum sprinkled salt, pepper and hot sauce into the frying pan. Just before the fish was ready he added thick slices of Bermuda onion. By the time they ate it was growing dark. Only a thin line of pinkish light glowed in the west, and this only added to the exhilaration of the moment. Sammy thought it was the best dinner he'd ever eaten.

After cleaning the dishes Nita announced that she was going to soak in a hot tub. Mr. Jum and Sammy stayed downstairs to watch television.

About midnight Sammy heard Dee Dee come home. She made a flamboyant display of going to bed, but then he heard her sneak Buddy Harrison and some other friends into the rathskeller. Sammy immediately went to the laundry chute. At first, all he could hear was some mumbling followed by intervals of silence. Then he heard music and the shuffling sound of feet on the linoleum floor as couples began slow dancing. He leaned his head against the laundry chute and listened to the music. After a while he dozed, dreaming of the time when he would be old enough to hold a girl in his arms, swaying gently to the soft strains of late night music on the radio.

The first signs that Nita was slipping were the lost chocolate chip cookies. Long after Dee Dee had left for college Nita continued to hide the cookies. It became a common occurrence to open a closet door and find a plate of stale cookies tucked into one dark corner. They were discovered behind the bread box, at the bottom of the dish towel drawer, buried under cans of vegetables in the pantry. It soon became apparent that Nita wasn't able to remember much of anything. She was sent to a doctor, who reported that her blood pressure was dangerously high. He put her on a daily medication that often made her drowsy, and did nothing

123

for her flagging memory. When the bug man sprayed for roaches he revealed a bundle of rock hard cookies behind the refrigerator.

The kitchen had become invested with roaches, and the bug man blamed it on the cookies. Mrs. Bailey decided that it was at last time to dismiss Mr. Jum and the ailing Nita. They were summoned to the living room where together they perched like frightened sparrows on the sofa. Nita's hands trembled involuntarily. Mr. Jum sat grim faced and tight lipped. They were old people who had reached the end of the line. Nita never quite grasped this inexorable truth, but Mr. Jum accepted it as merely another passage in his long life.

"We just think it's better if you retire," Mrs. Bailey said.

Her husband added, "We're all getting older."

Mr. Jum only nodded his head.

Nita said, "Hmm," smiling blankly into space.

"You used to climb those stairs to the third floor like a mountain goat," Mr. Bailey continued, looking at Mr. Jum. "But I hear you huffing and puffing to get up the stairs now. It's time you retired. You've earned it."

Sammy, a senior in high school now, had been listening from the front hall. Suddenly, he rushed into the living room with a wild look on his face. At once he took in the whole scene. The family, his family as he had come to view it, was on the brink of breaking up.

"If they go then I'm going with them," he announced angrily.

"Sammy!" his mother shrieked.

His father said, "Now, son, this doesn't concern you."

"It does too," Sammy yelled.

"I think you better leave the room. This is not your decision," his father said sternly.

"I'm not leaving this room." He stared hard at his father.

"Sammy---" his mother began.

"They're family!" Sammy shouted.

"It's time for us to go back to Paris," Mr. Jum said, his voice more of a whisper than ever.

"No," Sammy said, holding up his hand like a traffic cop. "This is your home."

There was a long, awkward silence. Finally, Mr. Bailey sighed loudly and realizing that Sammy would be going off to colleage in a year said, "Very well, you're welcome to stay."

Mrs. Bailey shot her husband a harsh glance that Sammy spotted.

"Don't you realize that they are as much my family as you are,

124

Mother? They've taken care of me just the same as you and Dad have for all these years. Mr. Jum is my best friend."

His mother closed her eyes for a long moment. When she opened them she smiled wanly and nodded her head, relenting. "Then we will remain a family," she said at last.

The next fall Mr. Jum cried when Sammy left for college. He sat on his stool in the pantry and tears streaked his cheeks. Sammy hugged him and rubbed his bald head affectionately.

"I'll be back for Christmas."

"Colorado is a long ways off."

"But I will be back."

Sammy rode the train from St. Louis to Denver. That night on the train when he opened his overnight bag he found six chocolate chip cookies wrapped in tin foil. It was late and except for a few tiny, pale lights in the ceiling the train car was dark. The countryside outside was black and desolate. Creation. That's what Mr. Jum called the land. Creation. Sammy ate one of the cookies and then, for no reason at all, began to cry.

Nita died in her sleep the following spring. Sammy wanted to come home for the funeral, but he had exams. He talked to Mr. Jum on the phone, who sounded older than usual and was barely able to talk. Sammy kept saying over and over into the phone, "I'll be home shortly, Mr. Jum. I'll be home shortly."

When Sammy arrived home for the summer his parents broke the news that Mr. Jum had been put in a state run nursing home. Sammy exploded in anger. He railed against his parents. He flounced about the room waving his hands in the air. He made threats: Mr. Jum would be moved back into the house immediately or else.

As it turned out Mr. Jum had suffered a stroke and there was no way he could have stayed in the house. He required full time care. One leg was completely useless. Sammy breathed deeply for several minutes, gulping in air the way a person does after trying to get rid of the hiccups. He sat dejectedly, staring blankly at the painting over the fireplace. The picture had been there for years, but he had never really looked at it. Now, he saw that it was a scene of a tree lined, cobblestone street that was wet with rain. Two people were crossing the street, sharing the privacy of an umbrella.

Sammy ran up to the third floor room. All the boxes that had lined the wall were gone. So was Mr. Jum's chair and the radio with its faded and cracked plastic housing. But there was still a presence in the room. Sammy could smell the Vaseline that Nita rubbed on her dry skin and into

125

her scalp. He could smell the remnants of pipe smoke and perspiration. On the floor he spotted a button that had fallen from one of Mr. Jum's work shirts and the beat of the Grand 'Ol Opry still thrummed in the room.

Sammy arrived at the nursing home about four in the afternoon. Mr. Jum was propped up in a straight back chair, a thin blanket stretched across his lap. He looked different, much older. A grey pallor was brushed across his sunken cheeks. He no longer held his head in the air as though looking for someone, and his shoulders slouched as though he'd been carrying a great weight for a very long time. He wasn't wearing his false teeth and his lips disappeared into his mouth. A television blared in one corner of the room. Several other patients sat fecklessly about the room either staring at the television set or off into space.

Sammy pulled up a chair and, sitting down, rubbed Mr. Jum's hand until the old man slowly blinked open his eyes. He smiled and very deliberately raised a hand to Sammy's face. He stroked a cheek with the back of his hand and then feebly reached behind Sammy's neck and pulled him closer.

"I love you," he whispered, his voice more husky than ever.

I love you, too, Mr. Jum."

Sammy stayed through dinner. Later, he helped an orderly get Mr. Jum to bed. He shared the bedroom with three other men. Sammy sat in the dark room holding Mr. Jum's hand, speaking to him softly, talking about the days when Nita was still alive and before Dee Dee had gotten married and moved to another city. Mr. Jum stayed awake until it was very late. The other men were asleep and the sound of their heavy breathing gradually filled the room. Finally, Mr. Jum joined them and Sammy heard the familiar rattling of his gentle snore.

Sammy quietly left the room. In the dimly lit hallway he saw a nurse sitting at a small, worn desk. He walked over and asked her what the doctors had to say about Mr. Jum.

"Who?" she asked. She gave him a tired look.

His name is Orlando Smith, but I've always called him Mr. Jum. He likes that name. Maybe everyone could call him that here."

Just then Mr. Jum could be heard screaming wildly at the top of his lungs. Sammy and the nurse rushed into the room. The nurse shined a flashlight into Mr. Jum's face.

"What's going on in here?" she demanded harshly.

"I had a bad dream," Mr. Jum said, his whisper a bit louder and more hoarse than usual. He blinked in the flashlight's glare.

Sammy pushed the light away. "I'll sit with him," he told the nurse.

When the nurse had left the room Sammy asked, "What happened?"

"I was watching the television today and there was a show on about snakes. I hate snakes. I'm scared to death of snakes. There was this one snake hiding up in the branches of a tree. Then this cat, like a lion or something, walked under the tree. The snake jumped out of that tree and wrapped hisself around that cat."

"You go back to sleep now."

"I'm afraid, Sammy."

"Don't be afraid, I'm here."

They held each other's hands in the dark. Several times Mr. Jum twitched as though startled. And then after a while he breathed deeply and his hand fell limp as he slept.

Sammy sat with him in the dark room for a long time. His thoughts drifted back to his childhood and he realized how much he missed those days. He thought about his parents, the fried chicken dinners that Nita cooked on Sundays, the time when he was only twelve and drove his father's car through the closed garage door. He remembered Dee Dee and their silly childhood arguments and how when she had been at home they had been a family, all together under one roof. He wished that there was only some way to recapture those times, those days of innocence and youth.

Finally, he crawled up onto the foot of Mr. Jum's bed, and curling himself into a ball, he closed his eyes and fell asleep.

127